OTHER FAST FACTS BOOKS

Fast Facts About PTSD: A Guide for Nurses and Other Health

Fast Facts for the NEW NURSE PRACTITIONER: What You Re (*Aktan*)

Fast Facts for the ER NURSE: Emergency Department Orientation in a Nutshell, ...

Fast Facts About GI AND LIVER DISEASES FOR NURSES: What APRNs Need to Know in a Nutshell (*Chaney*)

Fast Facts for the MEDICAL–SURGICAL NURSE: Clinical Orientation in a Nutshell (*Ciocco*)

Fast Facts on COMBATING NURSE BULLYING, INCIVILITY, AND WORKPLACE VIOLENCE: What Nurses Need to Know in a Nutshell (*Ciocco*)

Fast Facts for the NURSE PRECEPTOR: Keys to Providing a Successful Preceptorship in a Nutshell (*Ciocco*)

Fast Facts for the OPERATING ROOM NURSE: An Orientation and Care Guide, Second Edition (*Criscitelli*)

Fast Facts for the ANTEPARTUM AND POSTPARTUM NURSE: A Nursing Orientation and Care Guide in a Nutshell (*Davidson*)

Fast Facts for the NEONATAL NURSE: A Nursing Orientation and Care Guide in a Nutshell (*Davidson*)

Fast Facts Workbook for CARDIAC DYSRHYTHMIAS AND 12-LEAD EKGs (*Desmarais*)

Fast Facts About PRESSURE ULCER CARE FOR NURSES: How to Prevent, Detect, and Resolve Them in a Nutshell (*Dziedzic*)

Fast Facts for the GERONTOLOGY NURSE: A Nursing Care Guide in a Nutshell (*Eliopoulos*)

Fast Facts for the LONG-TERM CARE NURSE: What Nursing Home and Assisted Living Nurses Need to Know in a Nutshell (*Eliopoulos*)

Fast Facts for the CLINICAL NURSE MANAGER: Managing a Changing Workplace in a Nutshell, Second Edition (*Fry*)

Fast Facts for EVIDENCE-BASED PRACTICE IN NURSING: Implementing EBP in a Nutshell, Second Edition (*Godshall*)

Fast Facts for Nurses About HOME INFUSION THERAPY: The Expert's Best Practice Guide in a Nutshell (*Gorski*)

Fast Facts About NURSING AND THE LAW: Law for Nurses in a Nutshell (*Grant, Ballard*)

Fast Facts for the L&D NURSE: Labor & Delivery Orientation in a Nutshell, Second Edition (*Groll*)

Fast Facts for the RADIOLOGY NURSE: An Orientation and Nursing Care Guide in a Nutshell (*Grossman*)

Fast Facts on ADOLESCENT HEALTH FOR NURSING AND HEALTH PROFESSIONALS: A Care Guide in a Nutshell (*Herrman*)

Fast Facts for the FAITH COMMUNITY NURSE IN NURSING: Implementing FCN/Parish Nursing in a Nutshell (*Hickman*)

Fast Facts for the CARDIAC SURGERY NURSE: Caring for Cardiac Surgery Patients in a Nutshell, Second Edition (*Hodge*)

Fast Facts About the NURSING PROFESSION: Historical Perspectives in a Nutshell (*Hunt*)

Fast Facts for the CLINICAL NURSING INSTRUCTOR: Clinical Teaching in a Nutshell, Third Edition (*Kan, Stabler-Haas*)

Fast Facts for the WOUND CARE NURSE: Practical Wound Management in a Nutshell (*Kifer*)

Fast Facts About EKGs FOR NURSES: The Rules of Identifying EKGs in a Nutshell (*Landrum*)

Fast Facts for the CRITICAL CARE NURSE: Critical Care Nursing in a Nutshell (*Landrum*)

Fast Facts for the TRAVEL NURSE: Travel Nursing in a Nutshell (*Landrum*)

Fast Facts for the SCHOOL NURSE: School Nursing in a Nutshell, Second Edition (*Loschiavo*)

Fast Facts for MANAGING PATIENTS WITH A PSYCHIATRIC DISORDER: What RNs, NPs, and New Psych Nurses Need to Know (*Marshall*)

Fast Facts About SUBSTANCE USE DISORDERS: What Every Nurse, APRN, and PA Needs to Know (*Marshall, Spencer*)

Fast Facts About CURRICULUM DEVELOPMENT IN NURSING: How to Develop and Evaluate Educational Programs in a Nutshell, Second Edition (*McCoy, Anema*)

Fast Facts for the CATH LAB NURSE (*McCulloch*)

Fast Facts About NEUROCRITICAL CARE: A Quick Reference for the Advanced Practice Provider (*McLaughlin*)

Fast Facts for DEMENTIA CARE: What Nurses Need to Know in a Nutshell (*Miller*)

Fast Facts for HEALTH PROMOTION IN NURSING: Promoting Wellness in a Nutshell (*Miller*)

Fast Facts for STROKE CARE NURSING: An Expert Care Guide, Second Edition (*Morrison*)

Fast Facts for the MEDICAL OFFICE NURSE: What You Really Need to Know in a Nutshell (*Richmeier*)

Fast Facts for the PEDIATRIC NURSE: An Orientation Guide in a Nutshell (*Rupert, Young*)

Fast Facts About FORENSIC NURSING: What You Need to Know (*Scannell*)

Fast Facts About the GYNECOLOGICAL EXAM: A Professional Guide for NPs, PAs, and Midwives, Second Edition (*Secor, Fantasia*)

Fast Facts for the STUDENT NURSE: Nursing Student Success in a Nutshell (*Stabler-Haas*)

Fast Facts for CAREER SUCCESS IN NURSING: Making the Most of Mentoring in a Nutshell (*Vance*)

Fast Facts for the TRIAGE NURSE: An Orientation and Care Guide, Second Edition (*Visser, Montejano*)

Fast Facts for DEVELOPING A NURSING ACADEMIC PORTFOLIO: What You Really Need to Know in a Nutshell (*Wittmann-Price*)

Fast Facts for the HOSPICE NURSE: A Concise Guide to End-of-Life Care (*Wright*)

Fast Facts for the CLASSROOM NURSING INSTRUCTOR: Classroom Teaching in a Nutshell (*Yoder-Wise, Kowalski*)

Forthcoming FAST FACTS Books

Fast Facts About NEUROPATHIC PAIN (*Davies*)

Fact Facts in HEALTH INFORMATICS FOR NURSES (*Hardy*)

Fact Facts About NURSE ANESTHESIA (*Hickman*)

Fast Facts for the CARDIAC SURGERY NURSE, Third Edition (*Hodge*)

Fast Facts for the CRITICAL CARE NURSE: Critical Care Nursing, Second Edition (*Landrum*)

Fast Facts for the SCHOOL NURSE, Third Edition (*Loschiavo*)

Fast Facts on How to Conduct, Understand, and Maybe Even Love RESEARCH! For Nurses and Other Healthcare Providers (*Marshall*)

Fast Facts About RELIGION FOR NURSES: Implications for Patient Care (*Taylor*)

Visit www.springerpub.com to order.

FAST FACTS WORKBOOK for
CARDIAC DYSRHYTHMIAS
AND 12-LEAD EKGs

Paul L. Desmarais, PhD, RN, has been a practicing RN for 40-plus years, starting as an orderly at O'Blenness Memorial Hospital in Athens, Ohio, in 1975 and Good Samaritan Medical Center in Zanesville, Ohio, in 1976 and progressing to staff nurse in 1978 after graduating from Ohio University–Zanesville. He then worked his way up to become a staff nurse in the ICU at Nashua Memorial Hospital (later to become Southern New Hampshire Medical Center) and then charge nurse and nurse manager of the telemetry unit at Southern New Hampshire Medical Center in Nashua, New Hampshire. He was also the critical care coordinator and acting assistant chief nurse at the Veterans Administration Hospital in Manchester, New Hampshire, from 1983 to 1986. He obtained his bachelor's degree from St. Anselm's College in Manchester, New Hampshire, in 1984, followed by his master's degree in nursing, and PhD in nursing from the University of Massachusetts–Lowell in 2003. He continued to work as a bedside nurse even after he began his career as an academic teacher until he retired from bedside care in 2014.

He began his teaching career as an instructor in 1993 at Rivier College in Nashua, New Hampshire, and then moved to warmer climates in 2003 when he accepted a visiting assistant professor position at the University of Central Florida, focusing on critical care nursing and care of the adult patient. He remains at the University of Central Florida as an associate lecturer and continues to focus on critical care nursing while continuing to teach classroom and clinical courses with a heavy focus on caring for patients with coronary artery disease.

FAST FACTS WORKBOOK for
CARDIAC DYSRHYTHMIAS
AND 12-LEAD EKGs

Paul L. Desmarais, PhD, RN

SPRINGER PUBLISHING COMPANY

Springer Publishing Company, LLC
11 West 42nd Street
New York, NY 10036
www.springerpub.com

Acquisitions Editor: Elizabeth Nieginski
Compositor: Amnet Systems

ISBN: 978-0-8261-7503-8
ebook ISBN: 978-0-8261-7512-0

19 20 21 22 23 / 5 4 3 2 1

The author and the publisher of this Work have made every effort to use sources believed to be reliable to provide information that is accurate and compatible with the standards generally accepted at the time of publication. Because medical science is continually advancing, our knowledge base continues to expand. Therefore, as new information becomes available, changes in procedures become necessary. We recommend that the reader always consult current research and specific institutional policies before performing any clinical procedure. The author and publisher shall not be liable for any special, consequential, or exemplary damages resulting, in whole or in part, from the readers' use of, or reliance on, the information contained in this book. The publisher has no responsibility for the persistence or accuracy of URLs for external or third-party Internet websites referred to in this publication and does not guarantee that any content on such websites is, or will remain, accurate or appropriate.

Library of Congress Cataloging-in-Publication Data

Names: Desmarais, Paul L., author.
Title: Fast facts workbook for cardiac dysrhythmias and 12-lead EKGs / Paul
  L. Desmarais PhD, RN, Associate Lecturer, College of Nursing, University
  of Central Florida.
Description: New York, NY : Springer Publishing Company, LLC, [2019] |
  Includes bibliographical references and index.
Identifiers: LCCN 2018041218 (print) | LCCN 2018047103 (ebook) | ISBN
  9780826175120 (eBook) | ISBN 9780826175038 (print : alk. paper) | ISBN
  9780826175120 (e-book ISBN)
Subjects: LCSH: Arrhythmia—Problems, exercises, etc. | Electrocardiographs.
Classification: LCC RC685.A65 (ebook) | LCC RC685.A65 D47 2019 (print) | DDC
  616.1/280076—dc23
LC record available at https://lccn.loc.gov/2018041218

I have used the content of this manual for many years to help students grasp the concepts that are critical to understanding dysrhythmia recognition and 12-lead EKG principles. The information provided in this volume is a compilation of basic knowledge gathered from so many sources that acknowledgment of individuals is nearly impossible. Therefore, this volume is dedicated to all the instructors, nurses, physicians, patients, and authors with whom I have interacted over the years and whose brains I have picked. I was able to glean little bits from so many, and they were all smarter than I could ever hope to be.

Obviously, I owe a great deal to my family, especially my wife, Cecile, for putting up with my idiosyncrasies for so many years and for "slapping" me occasionally when I was at the verge of quitting. I would not be where I am today without her support.

Finally, to Dylan, the student who came to my office to insist that I put this volume out for publication. This is your fault, Dylan, and all the students who have to read this will be able to blame you. One more, "finally," to all the students who used this before it was a book and who supported Dylan. I'm glad that it was helpful to you all, and I hope that it will help others.

Contents

Preface

This workbook did not start out to be a workbook. As a typical egomaniacal critical care nurse, I believed that I had a duty to write the definitive book on dysrhythmia recognition. I actually did that and started the workbook, when the epiphany came to me that my "book" was basically the same as every other dysrhythmia book out there. Some are more in depth than others, but they all cover about the same topics and theories. I really did not have anything new to add. However, what always bothered me about those other books was their lack of actual guided practice.

Most of those other books provided examples and some practice, but most of the rhythms were textbook quality, which made them easy to decipher, and there were very few "demonstrations" of how to interpret them. As mentioned, I realized that my book was pretty useless, but a workbook, especially one that used actual rhythm strips, would be extremely valuable. Hence, the creation of this current tome. Not all the rhythms are actual patient rhythms, but most are. I found it difficult to find patients who would willingly provide me with some of the more lethal rhythms so that I could finish this book.

I was also bothered by the small amount of information that was out there on 12-lead EKG interpretation. What is out there tries to explain all the complexity of the 12 lead, and it can be very complex. This workbook tries to get away from that complexity and to simplify the process. In no way does it pretend to be the definitive authority on 12-lead interpretation. What it attempts to do is give the average nurse the tools to determine whether the patient is safe or not.

Most books will tell you that ST elevation indicates injury, whereas ST depression indicates ischemia. Hence, the dreaded ST-elevation myocardial infarction (STEMI) causes everyone in the emergency department to scurry for the thrombolytic drugs, whereas the person who presents with ST depression may be put on the back burner for a while.

Whether or not ST elevation indicates injury depends on the lead that the elevation is in and whether or not the elevation is an actual change or a reciprocal change. ST depression in leads V1 and V2 can actually be ST elevations in the posterior wall. It is right that we should respond quickly when ST elevation is present, but there is danger in ignoring ST depression.

The cause of ST depression is ischemia. ST elevation indicates myocardial cell injury, but the cause of the injury is ischemia. Both ST depression and elevation indicate ischemia. As long as ischemia is present, the patient is at risk for dysrhythmia and sudden death.

The purpose of the 12-lead EKG section of this workbook is not to make people experts in 12-lead EKGs, but to be expert enough to tell whether or not the patient is safe. The focus of the workbook is to help develop confidence in the reader relative to dysrhythmia recognition through practice. If the workbook does this, I will consider it a success.

The workbook is also designed to be used as a companion to almost every established dysrhythmia textbook published. It can be used as an addendum to any of the fine textbooks out there. As such, I offer it to you to help you provide safer patient care.

Paul L. Desmarais

General Rules and Procedures

Learning to recognize lethal and nonlethal dysrhythmias and to determine whether a patient is safe or at risk using a 12-lead EKG requires learning to use a systematic approach to interpretation. It is not mere recognition of dysrhythmia or learning what a picture means. It is gathering the right data to come up with the proper interpretation of the rhythm. This section provides the basic rules and procedures needed to begin basic rhythm and EKG interpretation.

In this section you will learn:

- Some basic rules of cardiology
- To measure appropriate interval spacing
- To recognize the origin of the P wave
- How to determine the type of heart block present
- The significance of the Q wave, ST elevation/depression, and T wave in the 12-lead EKG
- How the different leads of the 12-lead EKG relate to one another

1. When impulses arise from the same area of the heart and travel through the same tissue, they all look the same.
2. If impulses do not look the same, they are coming from different places in the heart.
3. If P waves look "normal" and consistent, they are assumed to be coming from the sinoatrial (SA) node.
4. P waves that do not look normal are coming from the atria. (All P waves come from the atria.)
5. If the P wave comes after the QRS complex, the impulse is arising from the area of the heart known as the atrial-ventricular (AV) junction.
6. If there is no P wave and the QRS looks nearly normal, the impulse is arising from the AV junction.
7. If the PR interval is less than 0.10 seconds wide, the impulse is arising from the AV junction.
8. If there is no P wave and the QRS is greater than 0.12 seconds wide, the impulse is arising from the ventricle.
9. The normal PR width is between 0.10 and 0.20 seconds.

10. If there are more P waves than QRS complexes, there is some type of heart block present.
11. If the PR interval is greater than 0.20 seconds and consistent and if every P wave has a QRS after it, the block is a first-degree block.
12. If there are more P waves than QRS complexes and the PR interval progresses in width before "dropping" a beat, the block is a second-degree block (Mobitz type I).
13. If there are more P waves than QRS complexes and the PR interval is constant in width when it is present, the block is a second-degree block (Mobitz type II).
14. If there are more P waves than QRS complexes and the PR interval is erratic in width, the block is a third-degree block (complete heart block).
15. For the 12-lead EKG:
    a. Significant Q waves (at least one fourth as deep as the R wave is tall or >0.04 seconds wide) indicate myocardial infarction if they occur in two or more related leads.
    b. ST elevation or depression indicates the presence of ischemia.
    c. Inverted T waves signify that something is going on and further assessment is needed.
    d. Related leads are:
        i. Leads II, III, and aVF (augmented vector foot) = Inferior wall
        ii. Leads V1, V2, V3, and (sometimes) V4 = Anterior wall
        iii. Leads I, aVL (augmented vector left), V5, V6, and (sometimes) V4 = Lateral wall

Workbook

1

Atrial Rhythms

The P wave is the key to determining from where a rhythm arises. Understanding this concept is central to all further interpretation. All P waves are produced in the atria. This includes sinus P waves because the sinoatrial (SA) node is in the atria. If all the P waves look the same, they are coming from the same place and going through the same tissue. If they look different, they are coming from different places and/or following a different pathway.

In this chapter, you will learn:

- To determine the origin of the P wave
- How to determine rate on a rhythm strip
- The terms *tachycardia* and *bradycardia*
- To determine whether a rhythm is regular or irregular
- The significance of certain "intervals"

RULES

1. When impulses arise from the same area and travel through the same tissue, they all look the same.
2. If impulses do not look the same, they are coming from different places.
3. If P waves look "normal" and consistent, they are assumed to be coming from the SA node.
4. P waves that do not look normal are coming from the atria. (All P waves come from the atria.)
5. Look for the "3-second" markers. The time between the first and third marker is 6 seconds.
6. To determine rate, count the number of complexes between the first and third marker (6 seconds) and multiply by 10.
7. To determine atrial rate, count the number of P waves in 6 seconds and multiply by 10.
8. To determine the ventricular rate, count the number of QRS complexes in 6 seconds and multiply by 10.
9. Rates greater than 100 beats per minute (bpm) are considered tachycardia.

10. Rates slower than 60 bpm are considered bradycardia.
11. Determine regularity (rhythm) of the strip by evaluating consistent time patterns between the same portion of adjacent complexes (i.e., P-P intervals or R-R intervals).
12. If the rhythm is irregular, determine whether irregularity is due to early (premature) beats or late (escape) beats or whether something is missing.
13. Evaluate P waves for origin. Ask these questions: "Do all the P waves look the same?" "Do they all have QRS complexes after them?" Remember that normal-looking P waves arise in the SA node. Those P waves that look different originate in the atria.
14. Measure PR interval. Normal should be between 0.10 and 0.20 seconds (2½ little boxes to 5 little boxes).
15. Evaluate QRS complexes. Ask these questions: "Do they all have P waves in front of them?" "Do they all look the same?" "Do they all look normal?"
16. Measure the QRS complex. It should be less than 0.12 seconds wide (three small boxes). Less than 0.12 seconds indicates rapid conduction through the ventricles using normal conductive pathways. Greater than 0.12 seconds indicates conduction defects/delays or travel through muscle rather than the normal conductive pathways.
17. Measure the QT interval. It should be less than one half the R-R interval. A greater QT interval indicates a delay in repolarization and increases the risk of arrhythmia production.
18. Normally, each QRS should have only one P wave. If there is more than one P wave per QRS and the atrial rate is normal, this is indicative of some sort of atrioventricular (AV) block.
19. If there is more than one P wave per QRS and the atrial rate is rapid, those P waves are not P waves they are F waves (flutter waves) and are diagnostic markers for atrial flutter.
20. If there are no P waves and the pattern is irregular, the diagnosis is atrial fibrillation.

RHYTHMS

EKG 1.1

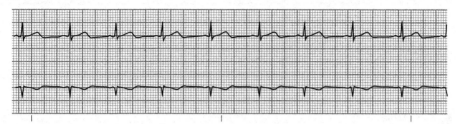

- Rate: Atrial _____ Ventricular _____
- Rhythm: Regular _____ Irregular _____
- P wave origin: _____
- PR interval: _____
- QRS: _____
- QT interval: _____
- Underlying rhythm: _____
- Variant: _____
- Diagnosis: _____
- Treatment: _____
  _____
  _____

Answer on page 126

EKG 1.2

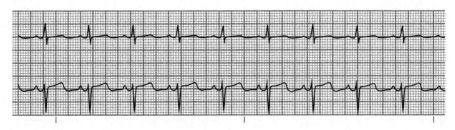

- Rate: Atrial _____ Ventricular _____
- Rhythm: Regular _____ Irregular _____
- P wave origin: _____
- PR interval: _____
- QRS: _____
- QT interval: _____
- Underlying rhythm: _____
- Variant: _____
- Diagnosis: _____
- Treatment: _____

_____

_____

Answer on page 127

EKG 1.3

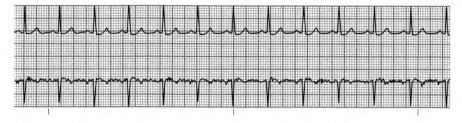

- Rate: Atrial _____ Ventricular _____

- Rhythm: Regular _____ Irregular _____

- P wave origin: _____

- PR interval: _____

- QRS: _____

- QT interval: _____

- Underlying rhythm: _____

- Variant: _____

- Diagnosis: _____

- Treatment: _____

_____

_____

Answer on page 128

EKG 1.4

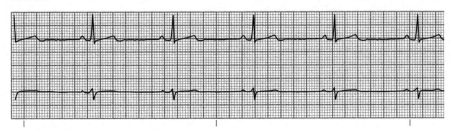

- Rate: Atrial _____ Ventricular _____

- Rhythm: Regular _____ Irregular _____

- P wave origin: _____

- PR interval: _____

- QRS: _____

- QT interval: _____

- Underlying rhythm: _____

- Variant: _____

- Diagnosis: _____

- Treatment: _____

  _____

  _____

Answer on page 129

EKG 1.5

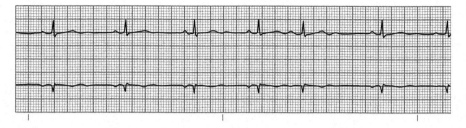

- Rate: Atrial _____ Ventricular _____
- Rhythm: Regular _____ Irregular _____
- P wave origin: _____
- PR interval: _____
- QRS: _____
- QT interval: _____
- Underlying rhythm: _____
- Variant: _____
- Diagnosis: _____
- Treatment: _____
  _____
  _____

Answer on page 130

EKG 1.6

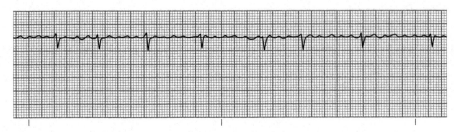

- Rate: Atrial _____ Ventricular _____

- Rhythm: Regular _____ Irregular _____

- P wave origin: _____

- PR interval: _____

- QRS: _____

- QT interval: _____

- Underlying rhythm: _____

- Variant: _____

- Diagnosis: _____

- Treatment: _____

  _____

  _____

Answer on page 131

EKG 1.7

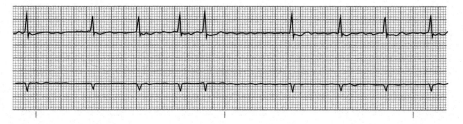

- Rate: Atrial _____   Ventricular _____
- Rhythm: Regular _____   Irregular _____
- P wave origin: _____
- PR interval: _____
- QRS: _____
- QT interval: _____
- Underlying rhythm: _____
- Variant: _____
- Diagnosis: _____
- Treatment: _____

_____

_____

Answer on page 132

EKG 1.8

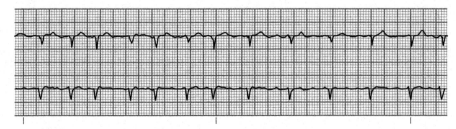

- Rate: Atrial _____ Ventricular _____

- Rhythm: Regular _____ Irregular _____

- P wave origin: _____

- PR interval: _____

- QRS: _____

- QT interval: _____

- Underlying rhythm: _____

- Variant: _____

- Diagnosis: _____

- Treatment: _____

  _____

  _____

Answer on page 134

EKG 1.9

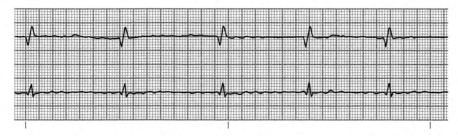

- Rate: Atrial _____ Ventricular _____
- Rhythm: Regular _____ Irregular _____
- P wave origin: _____
- PR interval: _____
- QRS: _____
- QT interval: _____
- Underlying rhythm: _____
- Variant: _____
- Diagnosis: _____
- Treatment: _____
  _____
  _____

Answer on page 135

EKG 1.10

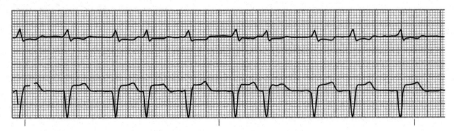

- Rate: Atrial _____ Ventricular _____
- Rhythm: Regular _____ Irregular _____
- P wave origin: _____
- PR interval: _____
- QRS: _____
- QT interval: _____
- Underlying rhythm: _____
- Variant: _____
- Diagnosis: _____
- Treatment: _____
  _____

Answer on page 136

2

Junctional Rhythms

In the old days, the rhythms described in this chapter were called nodal beats. *That's because it was believed that these beats arose from the atrioventricular (AV) node. Now the belief is that although some do arise from the AV node, many more arise from the tissue surrounding the AV node. The result is that the term has been changed to* junctional beats. *It's important to realize that part of the junction is in the atria and some is in the ventricle. This knowledge may make it easier to understand why junctional beats may have different configurations.*

In this chapter, you will learn:

- To interpret the point of origin for junctional beats
- How to tell the difference between a junctional beat, a premature junctional beat (PJC), a junctional rhythm, and an escape junctional beat
- The risks and treatments associated with junctional beats

RULES

1. If the P wave comes after the QRS complex, the impulse is arising from the junction.
2. If there is no P wave and the QRS looks nearly normal, the impulse is arising from the junction.
3. If the PR interval is less than 0.10 seconds wide, the impulse is arising from the junction.
4. If the junctional beat appears earlier than the next expected beat, it is a PJC.
5. If junctional beats appear in a row, the rhythm is a junctional rhythm and is usually present because the SA node is not functioning or is functioning slower than normal. This is known as an *escape rhythm.*
6. Everyone has PJCs from time to time, so infrequent PJCs are not of much concern. The more frequent they are, the more clinically significant they become. Frequent PJCs indicate that something has made the tissue in the junction more irritable. This can be due to ischemia secondary to heart disease, inferior wall myocardial infarction, heart failure, electrolyte disturbances, infections, medications such as digoxin, or ingested chemicals such as nicotine or caffeine (Bucher, 2014; Diehl, 2013).

7. If PJCs are infrequent, there is no treatment necessary. If they are frequent or the patient has symptoms such as hypotension, attempt to determine the cause and remove it. Digitalis administration is a common treatment, but because digitalis toxicity may be a cause of PJC, a digoxin level should be obtained prior to administration if the patient has been on the drug (Bucher, 2014; Diehl, 2011). Other medications that can be used are calcium channel blockers, beta-adrenergic blockers, and amiodarone (Bucher, 2014).

8. Unlike PJCs, a junctional rhythm is almost always an escape rhythm. It's there because a sinus rhythm is not. The exception to this comes when the junctional rate is greater than 60 bpm. In that case, the rate may be faster than the SA rate (or another way of looking at it is that the SA rate has become slower than the AV rate). In either case, this is not a rhythm that you would want to get rid of. By that, I mean obliterate the rhythm with the use of drugs such as amiodarone or lidocaine. If you do that, there may not be any other rhythm to replace it, and any rhythm is better than no rhythm. However, if the patient is symptomatic (having chest pain, is cool and diaphoretic, or is hypotensive, etc.), something must be done.

9. As previously stated, this is not a rhythm that you want to stop. This is a rhythm that you want to replace. The part of the heart that supersedes the AV node is the SA node, so the treatment of this rhythm is to kick-start the SA node. Atropine is the drug of choice followed by dopamine or epinephrine. If you get the SA node working at a rate faster than the AV node, it will regain control of the rhythm (Diehl, 2011). If the heart rate is slow enough, a pacemaker may be warranted. Often, however, if the junctional rate is fast enough and the patient is asymptomatic, this could be a rhythm to be watched in the hope that it will be self-limiting and the SA node will take over again. Prepare for possible pacemaker application (Diehl, 2011).

RHYTHMS

EKG 2.1

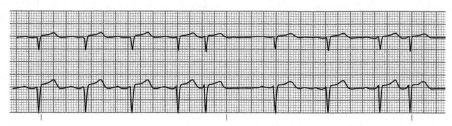

- Rate: Atrial _____ Ventricular _____
- Rhythm: Regular _____ Irregular _____
- P wave origin: _____
- PR interval: _____
- QRS: _____
- QT interval: _____
- Underlying rhythm: _____
- Variant: _____
- Interpretation: _____
- Treatment: _____

_____

_____

Answer on page 140

EKG 2.2

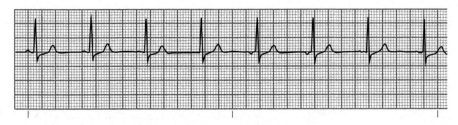

- Rate: Atrial _____ Ventricular _____

- Rhythm: Regular _____ Irregular _____

- P wave origin: _____

- PR interval: _____

- QRS: _____

- QT interval: _____

- Underlying rhythm: _____

- Variant: _____

- Interpretation: _____

- Treatment: _____

  _____

  _____

Answer on page 142

EKG 2.3

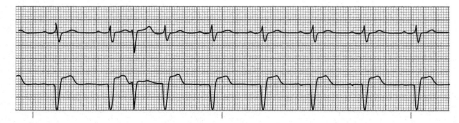

- Rate: Atrial _____ Ventricular _____
- Rhythm: Regular _____ Irregular _____
- P wave origin: _____
- PR interval: _____
- QRS: _____
- QT interval: _____
- Underlying rhythm: _____
- Variant: _____
- Interpretation: _____
- Treatment: _____
  _____
  _____

Answer on page 144

EKG 2.4

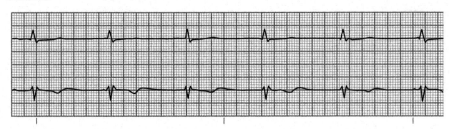

- Rate: Atrial _____ Ventricular _____
- Rhythm: Regular _____ Irregular _____
- P wave origin: _____
- PR interval: _____
- QRS: _____
- QT interval: _____
- Underlying rhythm: _____
- Variant: _____
- Interpretation: _____
- Treatment: _____

_____

_____

Answer on page 145

EKG 2.5

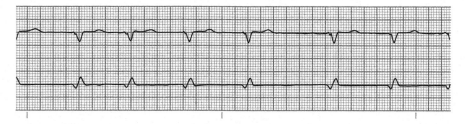

- Rate: Atrial _____ Ventricular _____
- Rhythm: Regular _____ Irregular _____
- P wave origin: _____
- PR interval: _____
- QRS: _____
- QT interval: _____
- Underlying rhythm: _____
- Variant: _____
- Interpretation: _____
- Treatment: _____

_____

_____

Answer on page 146

3

Heart Blocks

I cannot think of anything in cardiology that creates more angst in beginning students of cardiology than blocks do. As soon as the word "block" is spoken, I can see faces blanching, chins trembling, and an occasional grasping at the chest and gasping for air. Yet, blocks are, perhaps, the easiest of all the concepts in cardiology. They follow very specific rules, and because of that, they are easy to interpret. All the student has to do is to discard the stigma that seems to be attached to blocks, remember the rules, and apply them.

In this chapter, you will learn:

■ The rules needed to determine the type of heart block present

RULES

1. There are only three of them. There's a first-degree heart block, a second-degree heart block, and a third-degree heart block. Now, I grant that there are two types of second-degree heart blocks, but both are very specific.
2. With the exception of second-degree heart block (type II), they all involve the atrioventricular (AV) node. The AV node is not functioning as it should and has a hard time or is unable to allow impulses through to the ventricles. This is why they are known as *AV blocks.*
3. In a first-degree AV block, the AV node has been weakened. Perhaps it has been damaged by a lack of oxygen for a period of time, and that has made it ill. The SA node does not know that, and it continues to send impulses down at a normal rate. But because the AV node has been weakened, it has a hard time letting the impulse pass through to the ventricle, but it does. It only takes a little longer than normal. How long? More than 0.20 seconds. Remember that the normal PR interval is between 0.10 and 0.20 seconds. However, every P wave will have a QRS so the atrial rate and ventricular rate should be the same.
4. In a second-degree block, the AV node is even sicker so it will let some impulses get through, but it just cannot let others get through. The end result will be more P waves being produced than QRS complexes because some P waves are getting through (creating a QRS complex), whereas others are not.

5. In a third-degree heart block, the AV node is nonfunctional and does not allow any impulses through. The sinoatrial (SA) node does not know that, and it continues to send impulses normally. The ventricles, however, will not be receiving any of those impulses and assume that there is something wrong with the SA and AV nodes. As the third backup in the system, it will start acting as the pacemaker of the heart. The problem is that the normal heart rate for the ventricles is less than 40 beats per minute (bpm; remember that the AV node's base rate is 40–60 bpm). Therefore, the person will, essentially, have two hearts. One heart (the top one, or atria) will be beating 60 to 100 times a minute and the other (the bottom one, or ventricles) will be beating at a rate less than 40 bpm.

6. To recap:
   a. In a first-degree heart block, all the impulses get through.
   b. In a second-degree heart block, some impulses get through and some do not.
   c. In a third-degree heart block, no impulses get through.

7. **When there are more P waves than QRS complexes (but not at a rate that would make them F waves), there is some kind of block. The next step is to determine what type. To determine what type of block there is, examine the PR interval.**
   a. In a second-degree AV block (Mobitz type I), the PR interval gets progressively longer until a QRS gets dropped (there is a P wave with no QRS after it). So the PR interval of the first complex may be 0.20 seconds. The second complex might be 0.24 seconds. The third may be 0.30 seconds. Then there is a P wave with no QRS following it, and it did not "get through." Then the pattern starts up again: The first PR is 0.20 seconds, the second is 0.24 seconds, and so forth. The actual value of the PR interval is not important here. What is important is the progressive lengthening pattern before the actual dropping of a QRS complex.
   b. In a second-degree AV block (Mobitz type II), the PR is unchanged or "fixed," and then, for no apparent reason, there is a P wave with no QRS. Usually, the problem with a type II block is not in the AV node. Usually the problem is in the bundles. For that reason, a type II block is unpredictable. When it works, things are normal, including the PR interval. When it does not work, it does not work. The danger comes when it decides to "not work" more than it decides to work.
   c. In a third-degree AV block, the PR intervals make no sense at all. Some are wide, whereas others are narrow. Because the atria and ventricles are working independently of each other, the P waves just fall anywhere on the paper regardless of where the QRS complexes are. The result is PR intervals that have no pattern at all.

RHYTHMS

EKG 3.1

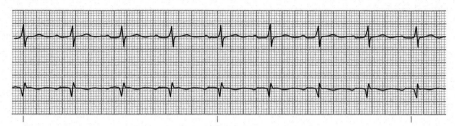

- Rate: Atrial _____ Ventricular _____

- Rhythm: Regular _____ Irregular _____

- P wave origin: _____

- PR interval: _____

- QRS: _____

- QT interval: _____

- Underlying rhythm: _____

- Variant: _____

- Interpretation: _____

- Treatment: _____

  _____

  _____

Answer on page 148

EKG 3.2

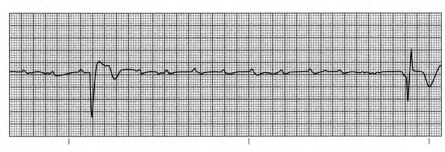

- Rate: Atrial _____ Ventricular _____

- Rhythm: Regular _____ Irregular _____

- P wave origin: _____

- PR interval: _____

- QRS: _____

- QT interval: _____

- Underlying rhythm: _____

- Variant: _____

- Interpretation: _____

- Treatment: _____

  _____

  _____

Answer on page 149

EKG 3.3

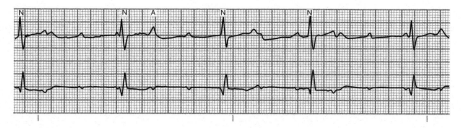

- Rate: Atrial _____ Ventricular _____
- Rhythm: Regular _____ Irregular _____
- P wave origin: _____
- PR interval: _____
- QRS: _____
- QT interval: _____
- Underlying rhythm: _____
- Variant: _____
- Interpretation: _____
- Treatment: _____

  _____

  _____

Answer on page 150

EKG 3.4

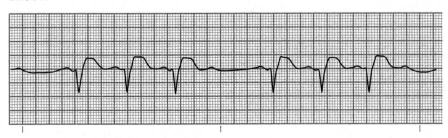

- Rate: Atrial _____ Ventricular _____
- Rhythm: Regular _____ Irregular _____
- P wave origin: _____
- PR interval: _____
- QRS: _____
- QT interval: _____
- Underlying rhythm: _____
- Variant: _____
- Interpretation: _____
- Treatment: _____

  _____

  _____

Answer on page 151

EKG 3.5

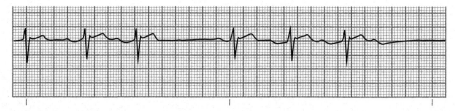

- Rate: Atrial _____ Ventricular _____
- Rhythm: Regular _____ Irregular _____
- P wave origin: _____
- PR interval: _____
- QRS: _____
- QT interval: _____
- Underlying rhythm: _____
- Variant: _____
- Interpretation: _____
- Treatment: _____

    _____

    _____

Answer on page 152

4

Ventricular Rhythms

Ventricular arrhythmias are usually the most lethal of arrhythmias. Fortunately, they are usually easy to interpret. They are usually large and ugly. A ventricular tachycardia has been described as looking at the devil's teeth. He is laughing at you as he is taking your patient away. Notice the use of the word "usually." In cardiology, there are few absolutes. Ventricular beats are no exception. What they look like depends on what part of the ventricles they come from. How you will treat them will depend on the patient's clinical picture.

In this chapter, you will learn:

- Why ventricular beats look the way they do
- The risks involved with ventricular arrhythmias
- How to determine whether a ventricular beat is dangerous or not
- Potential treatments for ventricular arrhythmias
- The difference between premature ventricular contractions (PVCs) and ventricular ectopic activity (VEA)
- The treatment for asystole

RULES

Ventricular beats are usually easy to detect.
1. They are usually wide and bizarre looking.
2. Second, there is no P wave. That's not exactly true, but that's what it looks like.
   a. The ventricles are composed of at least two different types of tissue. The conductive tissue is designed to conduct electricity, and it does so very quickly (less than 0.12 seconds). However, it does not contract very well. Fortunately, it makes up a very small percentage of the total mass of the ventricle.
   b. Most of the ventricle is composed of muscle tissue. It is designed to contract and squeeze and twist, and so forth in order to propel blood throughout the body. However, it does not like to conduct electricity. It will, but it does not like to. That's not what it's designed to do, so when it does it, it does it slowly. I mean s-l-o-w-l-y. This means that it takes longer than normal to create the QRS complex (greater than 0.12 seconds).

   c. As the ventricles are producing this large, slow complex, the electric impulse has time to travel backward through the atrioventricular (AV) node and into the atria, thereby creating a P wave, but because of the width of the QRS complex, it is rarely seen. The P wave is usually hidden by the QRS complex.

   d. Another characteristic of the ventricular beat is that it often looks "bizarre." That's due to two things: First, it looks wider than it actually is, and second, the T wave usually goes in the opposite direction of the largest deflection of the complex.

3. Idioventricular rhythms occur when both the sinoatrial (SA) node and AV node cease to function. If those two nodes stop working, the ventricles are designed to take over, but their rate is less than 40 beats per minute (bpm). That is not conducive to longevity, but it is preferable to no rhythm at all. Causes of idioventricular rhythms include myocardial ischemia, drug toxicities, and electrolyte disturbances, among others.[3,4]

4. Accelerated idioventricular rhythms are idioventricular rhythms that have a rate faster than the normal ventricular rate of less than 40 bpm. Technically, anything faster than 40 bpm would be a ventricular tachycardia (VT), but that would cause confusion since VT is a lethal rhythm that requires immediate treatment.

   a. An idioventricular rhythm that is faster than "normal" might actually be a good thing. The closer the rate is to a normal rate, the better the cardiac output should be. So, although I would want to eradicate a VT of 200 bpm as quickly as possible, I may not want to eradicate a ventricular rhythm that is at a rate of 90 bpm as quickly, but only as long as the patient tolerates this heart rate well.

   b. The real danger with accelerated idioventricular rhythm is that it might slow down and become simply idioventricular rhythm. If so, it might stop. The slower rate means less blood is being pumped and the risk for lethal ventricular rhythms and/or cardiac arrest increases.

   c. Sometimes, the healthcare provider will adopt a "wait and see" approach with this rhythm. As long as the rate remains stable and the patient is tolerating it, there is a chance that the issue causing this rhythm may resolve itself and the SA node may reassert itself. However, even if the provider opts for the wait-and-see method, atropine, epinephrine, dopamine, and the transcutaneous pacemaker should be readily available in case the rhythm decays into its slower form (Diehl, 2011).

5. PVC stands for *premature ventricular contraction*. This means it meets the criteria for being ventricular in origin (no P wave, wide and bizarre QRS), and it comes early (before the next expected beat). It's that simple. Beyond that:

   a. If all the PVCs look same, they are coming from the same part of the ventricle and are called *unifocal*. If they look different, they are coming from different parts of the ventricle (multifocal).

   b. If every other beat is a PVC, this is called *bigeminy*.

   c. If every third beat is a PVC, it is called *trigemini*.

   d. If there are two PVCs in a row, this is called a *couplet*.

   e. Three in a row is a *triplet* or it can be considered a short run of VT.

6. PVCs occur because there are areas in the ventricle that are "irritable" for whatever reason. That means they can depolarize sooner than expected. The irritability can be from electrolyte imbalances such as occur with hypokalemia; drug or medication effects such as result from cocaine, antidepressants, caffeine, or alcohol; cardiac infection; inflammation; muscle cell stretch due to fluid overload or cardiomegaly; and/or hypoxia (Bucher, 2014; Diehl, 2011).

7. **Significance**
    a. PVCs are not uncommon. Everyone has them from time to time. Too much coffee in the morning can cause them. Too little sleep can also be a factor. The point is not to panic when you see them. Yet they need to be evaluated.
    b. Some PVCs pump blood, whereas others do not. Which do and which do not depend on where in the ventricle they are coming from. If the PVCs are originating high in the ventricle, then the impulse needs to travel down toward the apex. That is pretty close to how a normal impulse would travel. In that case pumping may be near normal. If the PVC originates low in the ventricle, then the impulse has to travel up through the ventricle. That would be backward. This would mean that contraction would be backward as well, and no blood would be pumped.
    c. Chances are that any PVC your patient may have is going to fall in between the extreme high and the extreme low position in the ventricle. The key is to determine whether blood is being pumped. Take the patient's pulse while watching his or her heart rhythm on the monitor. If there is a pulse when the PVC occurs, the PVC is said to be "perfusing." If there is no pulse associated with the PVC, the PVC is not pumping blood and is not perfusing (Bucher, 2014).
    d. The number of PVCs is also a concern. If the PVCs are infrequent, there is usually no need for alarm. The more frequent they are, then the more "irritable" the ventricle is and the greater the risk of the PVC becoming a lethal ventricular rhythm such as VT (Bucher, 2014; Diehl, 2011; Sinz, 2011).
    e. Another factor to consider is how close the PVC is coming to the T wave of the preceding complex. When the R wave of a PVC strikes the T wave of a "normal" beat, the heart can go immediately into ventricular fibrillation (Comerford, 2016; Sinz, 2011). This is called the *R-on-T phenomenon* and is probably the main cause of death by dysrhythmia.

8. **Treatment**
    a. If PVCs are occasional and not close to the T waves of the patient's normal beats, they probably will not need treatment. However, if they are more than occasional or close to the T waves, the cause of the PVCs needs to be investigated. Perhaps the most common cause is hypoxia, so, if possible, the first order of treatment would be to administer oxygen (Bucher, 2014; Diehl, 2011).
    b. Electrolyte levels, especially potassium and magnesium, need to be examined and treated if necessary (Bucher, 2014; Diehl, 2011; Sinz, 2011). Medications, such as amiodarone, procainamide, lidocaine, and/or beta-adrenergic blockers, can be used for control of PVCs. However, hypoxemia is a major cause of PVCs (Sinz, 2011) and is perhaps the easiest cause to treat. If the patient is having PVCs, the first thing to do is to provide oxygen.

9. **PVCs versus VEA:** If the patient is in atrial fibrillation, abnormal complexes may look like PVCs, but they are not. The issue here is more in semantics than physiology. In order for something to be "premature" or "early," there must be a standard to measure from. With sinus rhythms, it's easy. The SA node provides a nice steady, regular baseline, and the ventricles produce a beat before the next expected beat (prematurely). That is not the case in atrial fibrillation. The base rhythm is chaotic. There is no standard, so when the ventricles produce a complex, it is neither early nor late. Therefore, it cannot be premature. It's the same animal, it just cannot be early. The proper terminology for these beats is ventricular ectopic activity (VEA). The treatment should be the same as for PVCs.

10. Unifocal PVCs have all the characteristics of PVCs (no P wave, wide and bizarre QRS complex, and they come early), but they all look the same. This means they are all coming from the same place and going through the same tissue. The

indication is that there is only one irritable focus in the ventricle. It is a priority to try to determine why that area of the ventricle is irritable and to try to correct the issue. If the PVCs are close to the T wave of normal beats, they could strike the T wave (R-on-T phenomenon) and cause ventricular fibrillation. If the PVCs are occasional, no treatment may be necessary. If, however, they are frequent or if they are coming close to the T waves, the cause of the PVCs needs to be investigated. Perhaps the most common cause is hypoxia, so, if possible, the first order of treatment would be to administer oxygen. Electrolyte levels, especially potassium and magnesium, need to be examined and treated if necessary (Bucher, 2014; Diehl, 2011). Medications, such as amiodarone, procainamide, lidocaine, and/or beta-adrenergic blockers, can be used for control of PVCs (Bucher, 2014; Diehl, 2011).

11. Multifocal PVCs are PVCs, but they do not look like each other. Because the PVCs do not look the same, they are coming from different places. That means there is more than one irritable focus in the ventricle. This is more serious than having only one irritable focus. There is a greater chance of developing VT or ventricular fibrillation. There is a little more urgency in treating multifocal PVCs than in treating unifocal PVCs. However, the criteria and treatment are otherwise similar. If the PVCs are infrequent, there may be no treatment. Otherwise, the first order of treatment would be to administer oxygen. Electrolyte levels, especially potassium and magnesium, need to be examined and treated if necessary (Bucher, 2014; Diehl, 2011). Medications, such as amiodarone, procainamide, lidocaine, and/or beta-adrenergic blockers, can be used for control of PVCs (Bucher, 2014; Diehl, 2011).

12. Bigeminal PVCs are PVCs, but they occur in a specific pattern. Every "normal" beat is followed by a PVC. In other words, every other beat is a PVC. Bigeminal PVCs may indicate increasing ventricular irritability (Diehl, 2011) and increase the risk of lethal arrhythmias such as VT or ventricular fibrillation. The first order of treatment would be to administer oxygen. Electrolyte levels, especially potassium and magnesium, need to be examined and treated if necessary (Bucher, 2014; Diehl, 2011). Medications, such as amiodarone, procainamide, lidocaine, and/or beta-adrenergic blockers, can be used for control of PVCs (Bucher, 2014; Diehl, 2011).

13. Trigeminal PVCs are PVCs, but they occur in a specific pattern. Every third beat is a PVC. Trigeminal PVCs may indicate increasing ventricular irritability (Diehl, 2011) and increase the risk of lethal arrhythmias such as VT or ventricular fibrillation. The first order of treatment would be to administer oxygen. Electrolyte levels, especially potassium and magnesium, need to be examined and treated if necessary (Bucher, 2014; Diehl, 2011). Medications, such as amiodarone, procainamide, lidocaine, and/or beta-adrenergic blockers, can be used for control of PVCs (Bucher, 2014; Diehl, 2011).

14. R-on-T phenomenon happens when the R wave of a PVC strikes the T wave of a preceding beat (Bucher, 2014; Sinz, 2011). Because the T wave occurs during the period when the cells are repolarizing, it is very hard to cause depolarization during the early part of the T wave as the cells are filled with sodium ions and no more sodium ions will fit. At this point, the cells are known to be "refractory." However, as the repolarization continues, more and more sodium comes out and the cells become less refractory. As more sodium comes out, the easier it is to put sodium back in, but it takes a stronger-than-normal impulse to cause the re-influx of the sodium. The energy from the PVC can cause that to happen. However, not all the cells may be at the same stage of refractoriness. If they are, they will all depolarize again and VT can occur. If they are not, some will depolarize and some will not, setting up a

situation in which depolarization and repolarization can occur randomly. This will cause ventricular fibrillation to develop. The R-on-T phenomenon is, perhaps, one the most serious of all the arrhythmias discussed so far. It cannot occur, however, without PVCs. The cause of PVCs, then, can lead to the R-on-T phenomenon. If R-on-T phenomenon does occur, it will lead to either VT or fibrillation. Either is lethal. Preventing or controlling PVCs will control the R-on-T phenomenon and prevent sudden death due to VT or ventricular fibrillation. For these reasons, PVCs are monitored for frequency and closeness to T waves. The first step in treatment is to administer oxygen. Electrolyte levels, especially potassium and magnesium, need to be examined and treated if necessary (Bucher, 2014; Diehl, 2011). Medications, such as amiodarone, procainamide, lidocaine, and/or beta-adrenergic blockers, can be used for control of PVCs (Bucher, 2014; Diehl, 2011). If R-on-T does lead to VT or ventricular fibrillation, basic cardiac life support (BCLS) and advanced cardiac life support (ACLS) protocols need to be started.

15. VT is the second most lethal rhythm possible. It is second because, unlike ventricular fibrillation, this rhythm can spontaneously correct itself. People can go into and out of VT without any obvious reason. VT also affects people in different ways. Often, the person in VT is awake and alert. At other times, the person in VT is unconscious. The difference is determined by where the tachycardia originates and whether or not the heart is pumping blood.

The brain is totally dependent on blood flow. If blood flow ceases, oxygen flow ceases, and the brain has little (if any) reserve of oxygen. The end result is that once the heart stops pumping blood, the patient loses consciousness immediately. After about 5 minutes of blood deprivation, brain damage occurs. After about an additional 5 minutes (10 minutes total), brain death follows. No matter the origin, if the VT is not stopped or does not spontaneously stop, it will eventually deteriorate into ventricular fibrillation. If the patient is awake, however, and there is blood pumping to the brain, there is time to treat this dysrhythmia with medication such as amiodarone or lidocaine. If the patient is unconscious, there is no time. This dysrhythmia must be treated by using BCLS and ACLS protocols, including electrical shock (defibrillation; Bucher, 2014; Diehl, 2011; Marcum, 2013; Sinz, 2011).

16. Torsades de Pointes is a specialized VT that is associated with prolonged QT intervals (Bucher, 2014; Diehl, 2011; Marcum, 2013; Sinz, 2011). It is often caused by magnesium deficiencies and may be prevented by ensuring that magnesium levels are within normal ranges. It is characterized by ventricular complexes that change in configuration and usually create a "bowtie" effect on the monitor. This is a lethal arrhythmia that should be treated as pulseless VT. Because it is a lethal arrhythmia, prevention is preferable to treatment.

17. Ventricular fibrillation is the most lethal and the easiest of all the rhythms to interpret. There are no P waves. There are no QRS complexes. There is no PR interval or QT interval or anything. That's the key. There is no rhythm. The patient is clinically dead. There is no pulse. There is no blood pressure. There is no blood flow to the brain. The patient will be unconscious. He or she will not be breathing. Life has ceased. He or she is clinically dead. This has to be stressed emphatically. Sometimes, a wire from the monitoring system will fall off, or an electrode will dry up and create a rhythm that looks like ventricular fibrillation. If so, the patient will be awake and/or breathing. If this is the case, do not shock him or her. He or she will become very upset. As with all rhythms, the critical element is to assess the patient. Again, do not shock if the patient is awake. If he or she is not responsive and is not breathing, begin CPR and defibrillate as soon as possible.

a. It's important to understand that during ventricular fibrillation the heart is not pumping blood, but that does not mean that the heart is not working. It is working very hard, but it is not working in a coordinated fashion. Something has happened to cause all the cells in the heart to depolarize and repolarize randomly. The end result is a lot of work being done, but the lack of coordination and cooperation leads to no effective end result or heart contraction (kind of reminds me of Congress).

b. The fact that work is being done leads to resources being used such as oxygen and glucose. Without blood flow, no more resources (oxygen and glucose) are being brought in. In the meantime, waste is being produced and there is no blood flow to carry the waste away from the heart tissue. Resources being used to create waste products (which again reminds me of Congress), but in the case of the heart, the accumulated waste leads to toxicity.

c. Most ventricular fibrillation begins as coarse fibrillation. As the heart becomes more and more toxic, the fibrillation becomes finer and finer until the heart completely stops.

d. In approximately 90 seconds (1½ minutes), the heart will be so toxic that it will not be able to respond to electrical shock. However, there is a solution to this problem. Oxygen must be replaced, and toxic waste must be removed. Blood flow and oxygen supply must be restored. The key to that is cardiopulmonary resuscitation (CPR).

e. CPR will not convert ventricular fibrillation back into a sinus rhythm. Only defibrillation will do that. The only way out of "V-fib" is to "D-fib." However, CPR (BCLS) will provide circulation and oxygenation enough to buy you time so that ACLS protocols and defibrillation can be successful.

18. Asystole is usually associated with the "flat line." I have always been amazed at how people die on television or in the movies. There they are lying in bed in a hospital somewhere with machines all around them and a heart monitor. All of a sudden, the monitor goes "flat line." A completely straight line appears on the screen and this loud screeching alarm goes off, and everybody starts running. You hear "Call a code" and then the room is full of people. Every time I see this, I realize that the program is full of something but it's not accuracy. The monitor does not go completely flat. There is always some activity from the heart: quivering, muscle twitching, or something that will cause some sort of artifact to show on the monitor screen. If the line is flat, someone disconnected it or the patient has been dead for so long that everything is cold and unmoving (like some of my former bosses). The fact is if someone is truly asystolic, there is no hope. Nothing is going to bring this person back. He or she is dead. But what if this is not asystole? What if, instead, this is a very fine ventricular fibrillation? We can treat ventricular fibrillation. If we think of asystole as a fine ventricular fibrillation, then our goal will be to convert the fine fibrillation to a coarse fibrillation so that we can defibrillate with a better chance of success. The drug of choice used to do this is epinephrine (Adrenalin). Epinephrine, however, will not work unless we get circulation going, so CPR will be required followed by ACLS.

RHYTHMS

EKG 4.1

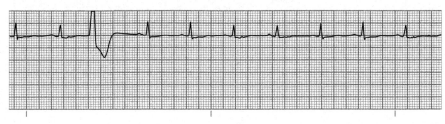

- Rate: Atrial _____ Ventricular _____
- Rhythm: Regular _____ Irregular _____
- P wave origin: _____
- PR interval: _____
- QRS: _____
- QT interval: _____
- Underlying rhythm: _____
- Variant: _____
- Interpretation: _____
- Treatment: _____

  _____

  _____

Answer on page 154

EKG 4.2

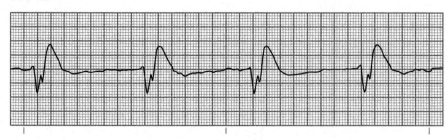

- Rate: Atrial _____ Ventricular _____
- Rhythm: Regular _____ Irregular _____
- P wave origin: _____
- PR interval: _____
- QRS: _____
- QT interval: _____
- Underlying rhythm: _____
- Variant: _____
- Interpretation: _____
- Treatment: _____

_____

_____

Answer on page 155

EKG 4.3

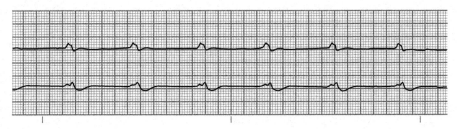

- Rate: Atrial _____ Ventricular _____

- Rhythm: Regular _____ Irregular _____

- P wave origin: _____

- PR interval: _____

- QRS: _____

- QT interval: _____

- Underlying rhythm: _____

- Variant: _____

- Interpretation: _____

- Treatment: _____

  _____

  _____

Answer on page 156

EKG 4.4

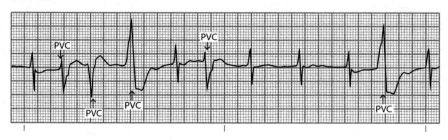

PVC, premature ventricular contraction.

- Rate: Atrial _____ Ventricular _____

- Rhythm: Regular _____ Irregular _____

- P wave origin: _____

- PR interval: _____

- QRS: _____

- QT interval: _____

- Underlying rhythm: _____

- Variant: _____

- Interpretation: _____

- Treatment: _____

    _____

    _____

Answer on page 157

EKG 4.5

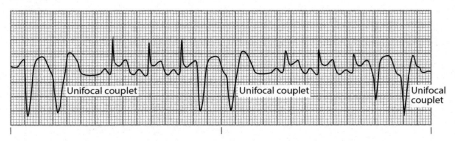

Source: Landrum, M. A. (2014). *Fast facts about EKGs for nurses: The rules of identifying EKGs in a nutshell* (p. 69). New York, NY: Springer Publishing.

- Rate: Atrial _____ Ventricular _____

- Rhythm: Regular _____ Irregular _____

- P wave origin: _____

- PR interval: _____

- QRS: _____

- QT interval: _____

- Underlying rhythm: _____

- Variant: _____

- Interpretation: _____

- Treatment: _____

    _____

    _____

Answer on page 159

EKG 4.6

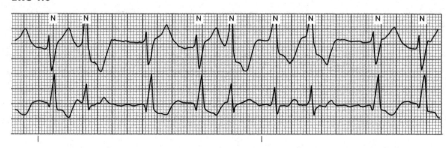

- ■ Rate: Atrial _____ Ventricular _____
- ■ Rhythm: Regular _____ Irregular _____
- ■ P wave origin: _____
- ■ PR interval: _____
- ■ QRS: _____
- ■ QT interval: _____
- ■ Underlying rhythm: _____
- ■ Variant: _____
- ■ Interpretation: _____
- ■ Treatment: _____

_____

_____

Answer on page 160

EKG 4.7

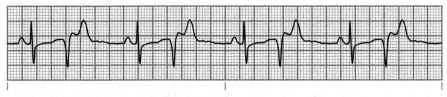

Source: Landrum, M. A. (2014). *Fast facts about EKGs for nurses: The rules of identifying EKGs in a nutshell* (p. 101). New York, NY: Springer Publishing.

- Rate: Atrial _____ Ventricular _____
- Rhythm: Regular _____ Irregular _____
- P wave origin: _____
- PR interval: _____
- QRS: _____
- QT interval: _____
- Underlying rhythm: _____
- Variant: _____
- Interpretation: _____
- Treatment: _____
  _____
  _____

Answer on page 161

EKG 4.8

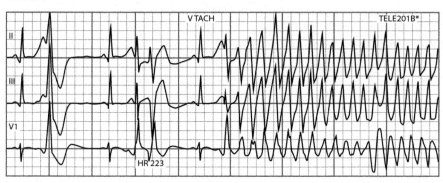

Source: Knechtel, M. (2017). *EKGs for the nurse practitioner and physician assistant* (2nd ed., p. 172). New York, NY: Springer Publishing.

- Rate: Atrial _____ Ventricular _____

- Rhythm: Regular _____ Irregular _____

- P wave origin: _____

- PR interval: _____

- QRS: _____

- QT interval: _____

- Underlying rhythm: _____

- Variant: _____

- Interpretation: _____

- Treatment: _____

    _____

    _____

Answer on page 162

EKG 4.9

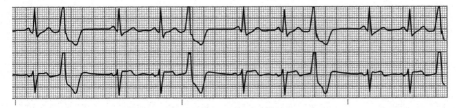

- ▪ Rate: Atrial _____ Ventricular _____

- ▪ Rhythm: Regular _____ Irregular _____

- ▪ P wave origin: _____

- ▪ PR interval: _____

- ▪ QRS: _____

- ▪ QT interval: _____

- ▪ Underlying rhythm: _____

- ▪ Variant: _____

- ▪ Interpretation: _____

- ▪ Treatment: _____

      _____

      _____

Answer on page 164

EKG 4.10

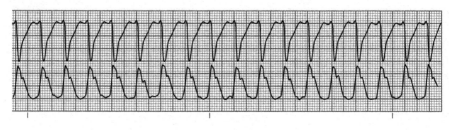

- Rate: Atrial _____ Ventricular _____
- Rhythm: Regular _____ Irregular _____
- P wave origin: _____
- PR interval: _____
- QRS: _____
- QT interval: _____
- Underlying rhythm: _____
- Variant: _____
- Interpretation: _____
- Treatment: _____

    _____

    _____

Answer on page 165

EKG 4.11

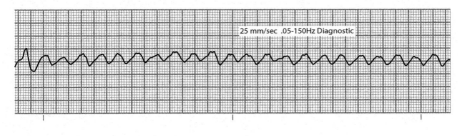

25 mm/sec .05-150Hz Diagnostic

- Rate: Atrial _____ Ventricular _____
- Rhythm: Regular _____ Irregular _____
- P wave origin: _____
- PR interval: _____
- QRS: _____
- QT interval: _____
- Underlying rhythm: _____
- Variant: _____
- Interpretation: _____
- Treatment: _____
  _____
  _____

Answer on page 166

EKG 4.12

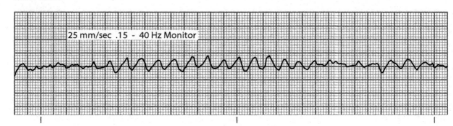

25 mm/sec .15 - 40 Hz Monitor

Source: Knechtel, M. (2017). *EKGs for the nurse practitioner and physician assistant* (p. 176). New York, NY: Springer Publishing.

- Rate: Atrial _____ Ventricular _____

- Rhythm: Regular _____ Irregular _____

- P wave origin: _____

- PR interval: _____

- QRS: _____

- QT interval: _____

- Underlying rhythm: _____

- Variant: _____

- Interpretation: _____

- Treatment: _____

  _____

  _____

Answer on page 168

EKG 4.13

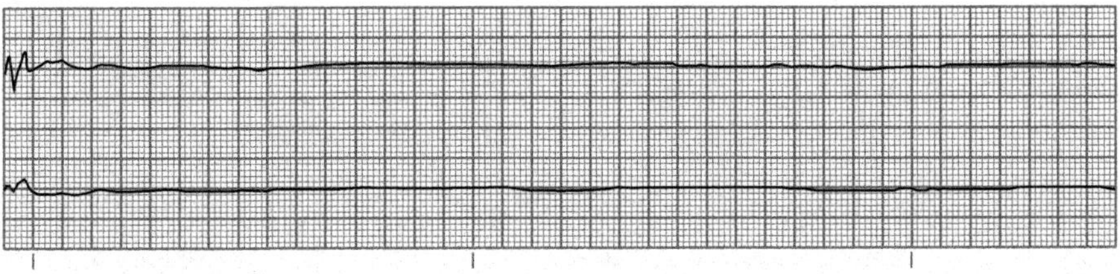

- Rate: Atrial _____ Ventricular _____
- Rhythm: Regular _____ Irregular _____
- P wave origin: _____
- PR interval: _____
- QRS: _____
- QT interval: _____
- Underlying rhythm: _____
- Variant: _____
- Interpretation: _____
- Treatment: _____
  _____
  _____

Answer on page 170

EKG 4.14

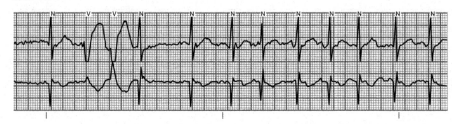

- Rate: Atrial _____ Ventricular _____

- Rhythm: Regular _____ Irregular _____

- P wave origin: _____

- PR interval: _____

- QRS: _____

- QT interval: _____

- Underlying rhythm: _____

- Variant: _____

- Interpretation: _____

- Treatment: _____

    _____

    _____

Answer on page 171

EKG 4.15

Source: Landrum, M. A. (2014). *Fast facts about EKGs for nurses: The rules of identifying EKGs in a nutshell* (p. 74). New York, NY: Springer Publishing.

- Rate: Atrial _____ Ventricular _____
- Rhythm: Regular _____ Irregular _____
- P wave origin: _____
- PR interval: _____
- QRS: _____
- QT interval: _____
- Underlying rhythm: _____
- Variant: _____
- Interpretation: _____
- Treatment: _____

    _____

    _____

Answer on page 172

EKG 4.16

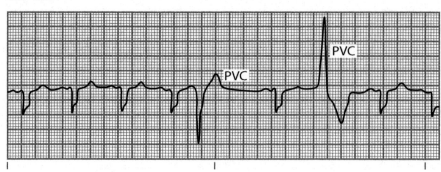

Source: Landrum, M. A. (2014). *Fast facts about EKGs for nurses: The rules of identifying EKGs in a nutshell* (p. 69). New York, NY: Springer Publishing.

- Rate: Atrial _____ Ventricular _____

- Rhythm: Regular _____ Irregular _____

- P wave origin: _____

- PR interval: _____

- QRS: _____

- QT interval: _____

- Underlying rhythm: _____

- Variant: _____

- Interpretation: _____

- Treatment: _____

  _____

  _____

Answer on page 174

EKG 4.17

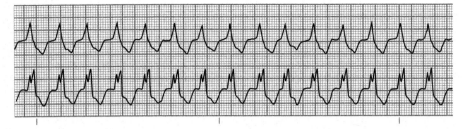

- Rate: Atrial _____ Ventricular _____
- Rhythm: Regular _____ Irregular _____
- P wave origin: _____
- PR interval: _____
- QRS: _____
- QT interval: _____
- Underlying rhythm: _____
- Variant: _____
- Interpretation: _____
- Treatment: _____

  _____

  _____

Answer on page 176

EKG 4.18

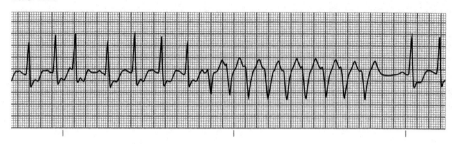

- Rate: Atrial _____ Ventricular _____
- Rhythm: Regular _____ Irregular _____
- P wave origin: _____
- PR interval: _____
- QRS: _____
- QT interval: _____
- Underlying rhythm: _____
- Variant: _____
- Interpretation: _____
- Treatment: _____

              _____

              _____

Answer on page 177

EKG 4.19

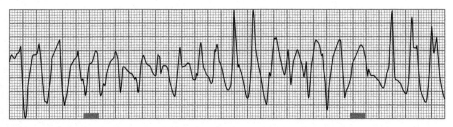

Source: Green, J. M., & Chiaramida, A. J. (2015). *12-lead EKG confidence* (3rd ed., p. 161). New York, NY: Springer Publishing.

- Rate: Atrial _____ Ventricular _____
- Rhythm: Regular _____ Irregular _____
- P wave origin: _____
- PR interval: _____
- QRS: _____
- QT interval: _____
- Underlying rhythm: _____
- Variant: _____
- Interpretation: _____
- Treatment: _____
  _____
  _____

Answer on page 179

EKG 4.20

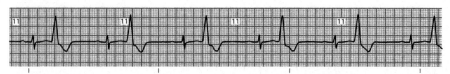

Source: Green, J. M., & Chiaramida, A. J. (2015). *12-lead EKG confidence* (3rd ed., p. 149). New York, NY: Springer Publishing.

- Rate: Atrial _____   Ventricular _____

- Rhythm: Regular _____   Irregular _____

- P wave origin: _____

- PR interval: _____

- QRS: _____

- QT interval: _____

- Underlying rhythm: _____

- Variant: _____

- Interpretation: _____

- Treatment: _____

   _____

   _____

Answer on page 180

EKG 4.21

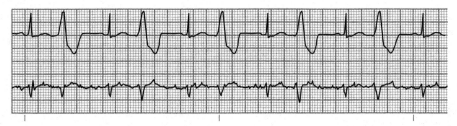

- Rate: Atrial _____ Ventricular _____
- Rhythm: Regular _____ Irregular _____
- P wave origin: _____
- PR interval: _____
- QRS: _____
- QT interval: _____
- Underlying rhythm: _____
- Variant: _____
- Interpretation: _____
- Treatment: _____

_____

_____

Answer on page 181

EKG 4.22

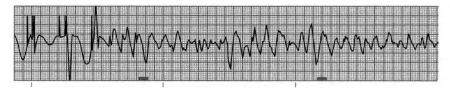

Source: Green, J. M., & Chiaramida, A. J. (2015). *12-lead EKG confidence* (3rd ed., p. 170). New York, NY: Springer Publishing.

- Rate: Atrial _____ Ventricular _____
- Rhythm: Regular _____ Irregular _____
- P wave origin: _____
- PR interval: _____
- QRS: _____
- QT interval: _____
- Underlying rhythm: _____
- Variant: _____
- Interpretation: _____
- Treatment: _____

_____

_____

Answer on page 182

EKG 4.23

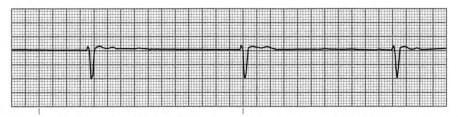

- ■ Rate: Atrial _____ Ventricular _____
- ■ Rhythm: Regular _____ Irregular _____
- ■ P wave origin: _____
- ■ PR interval: _____
- ■ QRS: _____
- ■ QT interval: _____
- ■ Underlying rhythm: _____
- ■ Variant: _____
- ■ Interpretation: _____
- ■ Treatment: _____
  _____
  _____

Answer on page 184

EKG 4.24

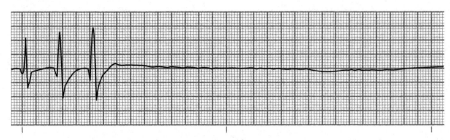

- Rate: Atrial _____ Ventricular _____
- Rhythm: Regular _____ Irregular _____
- P wave origin: _____
- PR interval: _____
- QRS: _____
- QT interval: _____
- Underlying rhythm: _____
- Variant: _____
- Interpretation: _____
- Treatment: _____

    _____

    _____

Answer on page 185

5

Paced Rhythms

Pacemakers are becoming more and more common in patient care. Understanding how to recognize the type of pacemaker that a patient has helps the nurse determine whether or not it is functioning properly.

In this chapter, you will learn:

- How to determine what type of pacemaker is present
- How to determine whether the pacemaker is functioning properly

RULES

1. Pacemakers pace. When they do, they produce a line on the EKG paper that is called a *pacing spike*.
2. Pacing spikes are supposed to produce contraction of the chamber being paced. This is called *capture*.
3. When pacing spikes capture the atria, they will produce a P wave.
4. When pacing spikes capture the ventricle, they produce a QRS complex.
5. To determine what type of pacing is being done, look to see what follows the pacing spike.
   a. If the pacing spike is followed by a P wave, it is pacing the atria.
   b. If the pacing spike is followed by a QRS complex, it is pacing the ventricle.
   c. If there are two pacing spikes, one preceding a P wave, and the other preceding a QRS complex, it is an AV (atrial ventricular) pacer pacing both the atria and the ventricle.
6. Pacemakers should not pace at the wrong time. A pacing spike striking a T wave is essentially a "man-made" R-on-T phenomenon and can lead to ventricular fibrillation.
7. It is important for pacemakers to be able to "read" the heart's own natural rhythm to prevent pacing at the wrong time. This is called *sensing*.
8. Dual-chambered pacemakers have one wire in the right atrium and one in the right ventricle.
9. Dual-chambered pacemakers can be configured to provide different functions.

a. The pacemaker can be programmed to pace both the atria and the ventricle (atrial/ventricular pacing).

b. The pacemaker can sense when the atria produces a P wave and then pace the ventricle at the proper time in cases in which AV node function is compromised (atrial sensing/ventricular pacing).

10. Automatic defibrillator pacemakers can sense the intrinsic heart rate and be calibrated to defibrillate the patient if a lethal dysrhythmia (v-tach [ventricular tachycardia] or v-fib [ventricular fibrillation]) is detected.

11. Paced beats are not "normal" beats. They are "man-made" and may look different. Most of the heart is composed of muscle. Normally, the electrical impulses of the heart travel down specific conduction pathways that are very fast (but do not contract well) and produce narrow complexes. Most pacemaker electrodes are placed on cardiac muscle and miss the conduction pathways. The results are slower transmission of impulses and wider complexes (especially ventricular complexes).

12. Sometimes atrial beats are very small and hard to see.

RHYTHMS

EKG 5.1

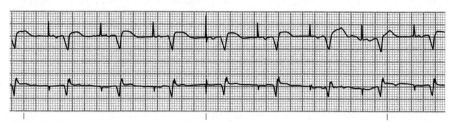

- Rate: Atrial _____ Ventricular _____
- Rhythm: Regular _____ Irregular _____
- P wave origin: _____
- PR interval: _____
- QRS: _____
- QT interval: _____
- Underlying rhythm: _____
- Variant: _____
- Interpretation: _____

Answer on page 188

EKG 5.2

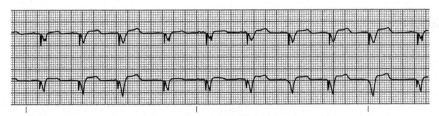

- Rate: Atrial _____ Ventricular _____

- Rhythm: Regular _____ Irregular _____

- P wave origin: _____

- PR interval: _____

- QRS: _____

- QT interval: _____

- Underlying rhythm: _____

- Variant: _____

- Interpretation: _____

- Treatment: _____

  _____

  _____

Answer on page 189

EKG 5.3

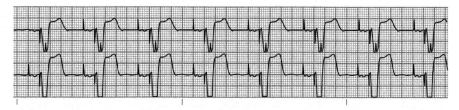

- Rate: Atrial _____ Ventricular _____
- Rhythm: Regular _____ Irregular _____
- P wave origin: _____
- PR interval: _____
- QRS: _____
- QT interval: _____
- Underlying rhythm: _____
- Variant: _____
- Interpretation: _____
- Treatment: _____

        _____

        _____

Answer on page 190

EKG 5.4

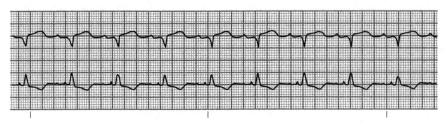

- Rate: Atrial _____ Ventricular _____

- Rhythm: Regular _____ Irregular _____

- P wave origin: _____

- PR interval: _____

- QRS: _____

- QT interval: _____

- Underlying rhythm: _____

- Variant: _____

- Interpretation: _____

- Treatment: _____

  _____

  _____

Answer on page 191

EKG 5.5

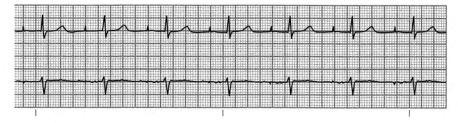

- Rate: Atrial _____ Ventricular _____
- Rhythm: Regular _____ Irregular _____
- P wave origin: _____
- PR interval: _____
- QRS: _____
- QT interval: _____
- Underlying rhythm: _____
- Variant: _____
- Interpretation: _____
- Treatment: _____

    _____

    _____

Answer on page 192

EKG 5.6

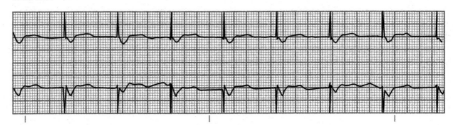

- Rate: Atrial _____ Ventricular _____
- Rhythm: Regular _____ Irregular _____
- P wave origin: _____
- PR interval: _____
- QRS: _____
- QT interval: _____
- Underlying rhythm: _____
- Variant: _____
- Interpretation: _____
- Treatment: _____

  _____

  _____

Answer on page 193

EKG 5.7

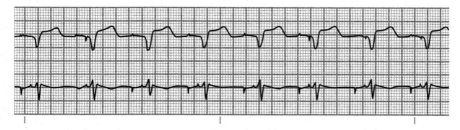

- Rate: Atrial _____ Ventricular _____
- Rhythm: Regular _____ Irregular _____
- P wave origin: _____
- PR interval: _____
- QRS: _____
- QT interval: _____
- Underlying rhythm: _____
- Variant: _____
- Interpretation: _____
- Treatment: _____
  _____
  _____

Answer on page 194

EKG 5.8

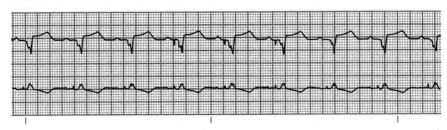

- Rate: Atrial _____ Ventricular _____
- Rhythm: Regular _____ Irregular _____
- P wave origin: _____
- PR interval: _____
- QRS: _____
- QT interval: _____
- Underlying rhythm: _____
- Variant: _____
- Interpretation: _____
- Treatment: _____
  _____
  _____

Answer on page 195

EKG 5.9

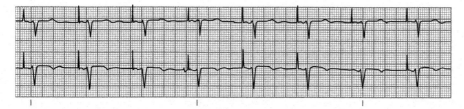

- Rate: Atrial _____ Ventricular _____
- Rhythm: Regular _____ Irregular _____
- P wave origin: _____
- PR interval: _____
- QRS: _____
- QT interval: _____
- Underlying rhythm: _____
- Variant: _____
- Interpretation: _____
- Treatment: _____

  _____

  _____

Answer on page 196

EKG 5.10

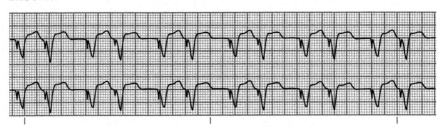

- Rate: Atrial _____ Ventricular _____
- Rhythm: Regular _____ Irregular _____
- P wave origin: _____
- PR interval: _____
- QRS: _____
- QT interval: _____
- Underlying rhythm: _____
- Variant: _____
- Interpretation: _____
- Treatment: _____

_____

_____

Answer on page 197

EKG 5.11

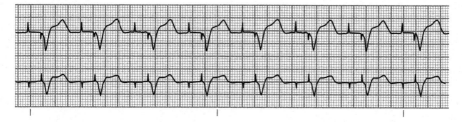

- ■ Rate: Atrial _____ Ventricular _____
- ■ Rhythm: Regular _____ Irregular _____
- ■ P wave origin: _____
- ■ PR interval: _____
- ■ QRS: _____
- ■ QT interval: _____
- ■ Underlying rhythm: _____
- ■ Variant: _____
- ■ Interpretation: _____
- ■ Treatment: _____
  _____
  _____

Answer on page 198

EKG 5.12

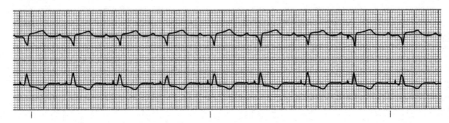

- Rate: Atrial _____ Ventricular _____

- Rhythm: Regular _____ Irregular _____

- P wave origin: _____

- PR interval: _____

- QRS: _____

- QT interval: _____

- Underlying rhythm: _____

- Variant: _____

- Interpretation: _____

Answer on page 199

6

12-Lead EKGs

There was a time when nurses had very little to do with the 12-lead EKG. If a patient had chest pain, the nurse would call the doctor. The doctor would order a 12-lead EKG. The EKG technician would perform the procedure and place a copy of the EKG in the patient's chart for the doctor to see when he or she came in next. That is no longer the expected standard. When the patient has chest discomfort, the nurse is expected to perform or order the EKG and evaluate the result to determine whether the patient is safe or not. That is all this chapter is designed to do: to teach you to evaluate EKGs. Nurses are not cardiologists, but they need to know what to look for in order to determine the level of risk for the patient. The patient's life may depend on it.

In this chapter, you will learn:

- How to tell whether the patient has had or is having a heart attack
- To determine whether the patient is at risk for lethal arrhythmias
- Techniques used to tell whether the patient's heart attack is old or new
- How to tell what type of heart attack the patient may be having
- How to detect the presence of an axis shift

RULES

1. This section does not make you an expert in reading EKGs. It is designed to allow you to make quick evaluations in order to determine whether the patient is safe or at risk.
2. There are three things to look for on the 12-lead EKG:
   a. Q waves: If significant, they can mean the presence of a heart attack (myocardial Infarction [MI]). In order to be significant, the Q wave must be one fourth or more as deep as the R wave is tall or greater than 0.04 seconds in width.
   b. ST elevation or depression: Elevation and depression both indicate the presence of ischemia. (In most texts, elevation equates with injury and depression equates with ischemia. However, that really depends on the lead you are looking at and whether or not the elevation/ischemia is an actual change or a reciprocal change.

At any rate, the injury is also caused by ischemia, and it is ischemia that places the patient at risk for arrhythmia and sudden death.)

   c. T wave inversion: Usually this is an indication that something is going on with the heart and must be evaluated further.

3. Each lead is evaluated for these changes.

4. Definitions

   a. Q wave: The first negative deflection of the QRS complex that is not preceded by an R wave

   b. R wave: The first positive deflection of the QRS complex

   c. S wave: The first negative deflection of the QRS complex that is preceded by an R wave

5. In order to be diagnostic, the presence of Q waves, ST elevation/depression, or T wave inversions must occur in at least two related leads.

6. Related leads look at the same part of the heart:

   a. Leads I, aVL (augmented vector left), V5, V6, and sometimes V4: Lateral wall

   b. Leads II, III, and aVF (augmented vector foot): Inferior wall

   c. Leads V1, V2, V3, and sometimes V4: Anterior wall

7. Q waves in V2 and V3 would be indicative of an anterior wall MI. Q waves in leads I and V1 would not be diagnostic because leads I and V1 do not look at the same part of the heart.

8. Lead V4 is considered a "transitional lead" and can be either anterior or lateral depending on patient size, size of the patient's heart, and actual positioning of the lead on the patient's chest.

9. If lead I and lead aVF are both predominantly positive in their deflection, the patient has normal conduction of the mean cardiac vector and the axis is considered to be normal.

10. If lead I is predominantly positive and lead aVF is predominantly negative, the mean cardiac vector axis is said to be shifted to the left.

11. If lead aVF is predominantly positive and lead I is predominantly negative, the mean cardiac vector axis is said to be shifted to the right.

12. ST elevation or depression is determined by the J point of the complex. If the J point is above the isoelectric line, determined by the PR segment, the ST is said to be elevated. If the J point is below the isoelectric line, the ST is said to be depressed. So how does it work (Figures 6.1 and 6.2)?

In the upper portion of Figure 6.1, the R wave is returning directly to baseline as it should. In the bottom illustration, the return changes direction. The point where it

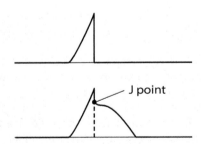

Figure 6.1 The wave should return directly to the baseline. If it does not, the point where the wave changes direction is the "J point." If the J point is above the isoelectric line, the ST segment is elevated.

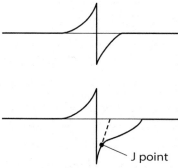

Figure 6.2 The wave should return directly to the baseline. If it does not, the point where the wave changes direction is the "J point." If the J point is below the isoelectric line, the ST segment is depressed.

changes direction is considered the J point. This J point is above the isoelectric line, so the ST segment is elevated.

In the upper portion of Figure 6.2, the S wave is returning directly to baseline as it should. In the bottom image, the return changes direction. The point where it changes direction is considered the J point. This J point is below the isoelectric line, so the ST segment is depressed.

When looking at the ST segment, remember that an elevation or depression is a sign of ischemia. The cure is to get oxygen supply to equal oxygen need. A Q wave is a sign that the ischemia was severe enough to cause tissue death. There is no cure for this. All the practitioner can do at this point is to get the oxygen supply to equal the oxygen need in order to prevent further tissue death.

In Figure 6.3, a large Q wave is noted. This indicates that tissue death has occurred. However, we can introduce a new concept here. Remember that the cause of tissue death is ischemia, and the indicator of ischemia is the ST segment. Also, once a Q wave has formed, it never goes away (although it will get smaller as scar tissue forms). So in Figure 6.3 we can determine that the Q wave results from an old infarction. We can determine this because the isoelectric ST segment indicates that there is no ischemia, and therefore, there is no reason for a new Q wave to be present at this time.

The presence of the Q wave indicates that an MI has occurred. However, the isoelectric ST segment indicates that there is no ischemia present at this time and that this MI is "old."

Figure 6.4 indicates the presence of ischemia, but there is no Q wave, so an MI has not occurred yet. If we do not balance the oxygen supply and demand, however, an infarct may occur and create a Q wave, or, worse, the ischemia can lead to arrhythmia and possible death. ST elevation indicates the presence of ischemia, but the lack of a Q wave indicates that the MI has not yet occurred.

However, it is possible to have a history of heart attack (Q wave) and to have new ischemia (Figure 6.5). When that is the case, there will be a Q wave and ST elevation or depression. There are two options: (a) Either there is an old MI and new ischemia, or (b) the ischemia is causing the Q wave to develop. The patient is having a heart attack right before your eyes.

In order to tell which is happening, the practitioner needs to evaluate old EKGs to see whether a Q wave was evident before. The difference, however, is academic in nature. If the practitioner does not treat the ST segment, the patient may have another MI and the Q wave may become larger. Even more important, the patient is demonstrating the presence of ischemia, and the ischemia will increase the risk of dysrhythmia and sudden death. Sudden death is much worse and much more permanent than having an MI.

Figure 6.3 The Q wave indicates the presence of an MI. However, the ST segment is isoelectric indicating the lack of ischemia needed to cause an MI. The interpretation, then, is that the MI is old.

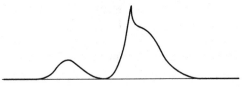

Figure 6.4 The ST elevation indicates the presence of ischemia. However, there is no Q wave, so an MI has not occurred. If untreated, an MI may result or the patient may develop dysrhythmia and sudden death may occur.

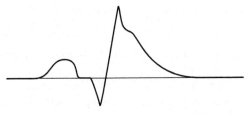

Figure 6.5 The Q wave indicates the presence of an MI. The ST elevation indicates the presence of ischemia. The ischemia may be causing the MI or the MI may be old with new ischemia present. The ischemia places the patient at risk for sudden death.

AXIS DEVIATION

One would think that the 12-lead EKG would be the definitive test for heart attack. It is not. The 12-lead EKG only looks at 12 different parts of the heart. It is quite possible for it to miss that part of the heart where the heart attack is occurring. There are also some types of heart attacks that do not produce a Q wave. So what good is this test?

It is important to realize that there is no perfect indicator of MI. Even cardiac enzyme markers can be misleading. The point is that the person caring for cardiac patients must be able to gather as much data as possible to come to a conclusion. The patient's clinical picture, history, and risk factors are just as important as lab tests and an EKG.

One of the tools that we can use to gather information is gotten by determining the axis deviation of the EKG. In order to be able to use this information effectively, it must be understood. In order to understand it, the reader will have to know that I lied earlier in this book when I said that the cardiac impulse traveled in a certain manner (Figure 6.6).

The impulse traveling down the heart does not follow a linear trajectory. Once a cell depolarizes, it depolarizes all the cells around it. Instead of following a straight line, the impulse radiates like ripples do after a marble is dropped in a pail of water. The impulse ripples through the heart muscle (Figure 6.7).

The machines that we use to monitor a patient's heart cannot read all of those impulses, so what they give is an algebraic sum of those impulses, known as the *mean*.

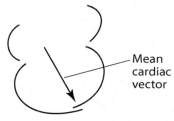

Figure 6.6 The cardiac monitors cannot show all of the vectors produced by cardiac depolarization. Instead, they take an algebraic sum to produce the "mean cardiac vector."

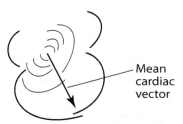

Figure 6.7 The mean cardiac vector is the algebraic sum of all of the cells being depolarized in the heart.

Understanding this is the crux of EKG theory. The mean cardiac vector is exactly what it seems to be. It is the mean, or average, of the impulses being produced. Because it's the mean, it must lie in the middle of all those depolarizing cells. This means the mean must have the same number of cells on one side of it as it does on the other (Figure 6.8).

A heart attack, or MI, is the death of cells. So when a heart attack happens, the balance between those cells is off (Figure 6.9).

But this is mathematically impossible. The mean must be in the middle. For this reason, the mean vector must shift until the number of cells is the same on both sides (Figure 6.10).

Therefore, if someone has a heart attack on the right side of the heart, the expectation would be that the mean cardiac vector would shift to the left to look for more cells to balance itself. By the same token, if the person has a left-sided heart attack, the mean cardiac vector should shift to the right in search of cells to create the necessary balance.

Unfortunately, there are things that can cause a shift in cardiac vector other than the loss of cells. If the patient should gain cells, such as with cardiomegaly, the vector will need to shift again to keep the number of cells equal on both sides of itself. So if an EKG shows a leftaxis deviation, the possibilities include (a) a right-sided heart attack or (b) left-sided cardiomegaly. A chest x-ray may help. If the patient does not have cardiomegaly, it increases the chances that the shift was caused by a loss of cells.

If the person has a right axis shift, the possibilities include (a) a left-sided heart attack or (b) right-sided cardiomegaly. It is possible to have a heart attack, causing a shift of cells away from that side of the heart, and also have cardiomegaly on that same side, thereby pulling the axis back into the "normal" region.

Add to this the fact that we can have axis shifts that are not shifts at all. Most women have normal axis deviation (NAD). This changes when they become pregnant and the infant pushes up against the diaphragm, causing an actual change in the cardiac position. The cardiac function will not change, but the axis will appear shifted on the EKG

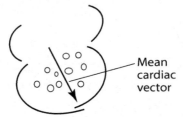

Figure 6.8 The mean cardiac vector must have the same number of active cells on either side of it.

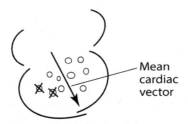

Figure 6.9 A heart attack (myocardial infarction) is death of cardiac cells.

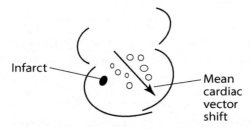

Figure 6.10 The loss of cells on one side of the heart will cause the mean cardiac vector to shift in the opposite direction until the number of cells is the same on both sides.

as a reflection of the actual change in the heart's position. The same is true for people who are obese or who have sudden weight loss. The axis shifts because of the changes in body habitus.

The axis deviation, then, is not a foolproof diagnostic test. It is merely another tool in our toolkit used to try to determine the patient's condition. It must be used with other tools such as cardiac enzyme levels, patient history, clinical presentation, and the 12-lead EKG.

DETERMINING AXIS DEVIATION

Determining axis deviation is not difficult, but it does require an understanding of how the deviation is determined. I have been to many classes that have taught me "tricks" that should help me remember, and I have always left those courses thinking that I finally "got it" only to be confused later. Knowing how to actually figure it out is longer lasting.

The first thing to remember is that the 12-lead EKG recording is made up of little lines, dots, squares, and so forth, and is actually printed on graph paper. The rhythms

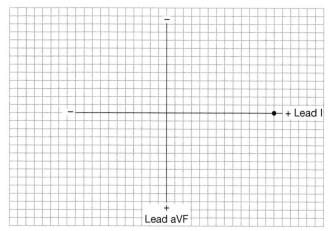

Figure 6.11 Lead placements for lead I and lead aVF are perpendicular to one another. If placed on a graph, it would look like this. Note how the positive for lead aVF is at the bottom.

aVF, augmented vector foot.

that we see are actually little graphs. The isoelectric line is the zero line of the graph. Anything above the isoelectric line is positive, and anything below it is negative.

In order to set up the graph, two leads are required and should be placed perpendicular to one another. When connecting the patient to lead I, the negative wire goes on the right arm and the positive wire goes on the left arm. If the arms are held up and away from the body, they form a straight line from right to left.

Lead aVF runs perpendicular to lead I. The positive electrode is on the leg, and the negative is theoretically on the forehead. The key here is to remember that the positive electrode goes down for aVF. On most graphs, the Y axis is positive above the X axis, but in this case it is positive below the X axis (Figure 6.11).

To determine the axis of the 12-lead EKG shown in Figure 6.12, we would need to count the number of boxes above and below the isoelectric line of leads I and aVF to determine an algebraic sum.

The first step would be to look at the impulse in lead I (Figure 6.13).

The PR segment represents the isoelectric line. There is literally nothing below it so the negative number is zero. The R wave, however, goes up for 13 boxes (millivolts): 13 − 0 = 13. The next step is to mark 13 boxes on the graph (Figure 6.14).

Next, the same thing needs to be done using the impulse in lead aVF (Figure 6.15).

Again there is nothing below the isoelectric line but about nine boxes appear above the isoelectric line. This needs to be plotted on the graph, but remember that, in aVF, the positive electrode is placed on the lower leg (Figure 6.16).

Now it is a matter of connecting the dots. Perpendicular lines are drawn from each point. Where they intersect will determine the direction of the vector (Figure 6.17). Because the vector always starts at the center (origin) of the graph, we can determine the vector's direction (Figure 6.18).

When the vector runs in this quadrant, it is considered normal. This would be known as a normal axis deviation (NAD). It runs approximately in the same direction as the normal cardiac vector would run. If the axis direction were in the upper-right corner of the graph, it would be considered a left axis deviation (think of how the heart is sitting in the patient's chest). This could be caused by a right-sided heart attack or left-sided heart enlargement. If the vector ran through the lower-left quadrant, it would be considered a

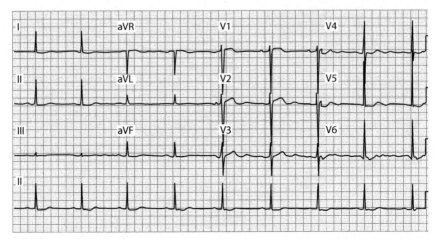

Figure 6.12 In order to determine the mean cardiac axis, we need to count the number of boxes above and below the complexes in leads I and aVF.

aVF, augmented vector foot; aVL, augmented vector left; aVR, augmented vector right; V, vector.

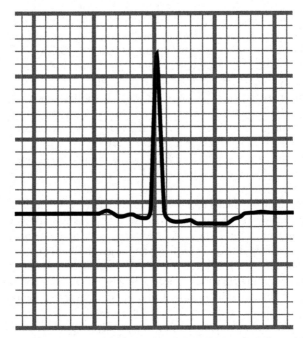

Figure 6.13 The PR segment represents the isoelectric line. There is literally nothing below it, so the negative number is zero. The R wave, however, goes up for 13 boxes (millivolts): $13 - 0 = 13$.

right axis deviation. This is often caused by a left-sided heart attack or right-sided heart enlargement.

It is very rare to see the vector running through the upper-left-quadrant. This is known as either *extreme left axis deviation* or *extreme right axis deviation*. Either way, it implies that the heart is pumping backward. Not something usually associated with longevity (Figure 6.19).

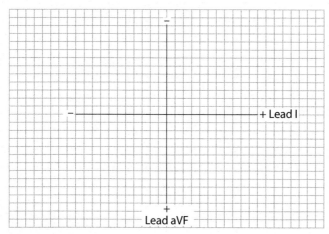

Figure 6.14 The next step is to mark 13 boxes on the graph.

aVF, augmented vector foot.

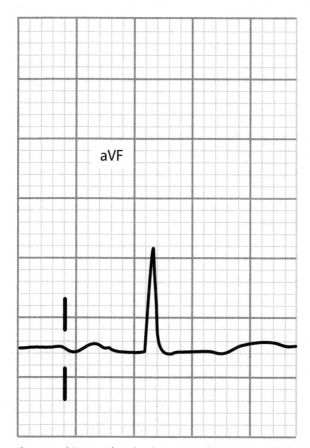

Figure 6.15 Next, the same thing needs to be done using the impulse in lead aVF (Figure 6.15). Again there is nothing below the isoelectric line, but about nine boxes appear above the isoelectric line.

aVF, augmented vector foot.

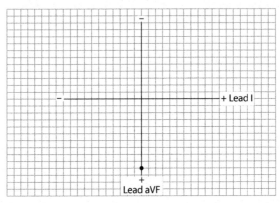

Figure 6.16 The algebraic sum of boxes obtained in aVF needs to be plotted on the graph, but remember that, in aVF, the positive electrode is placed on the lower leg so the positive on the graph is on the lower portion of the aVF axis.

aVF, augmented vector foot.

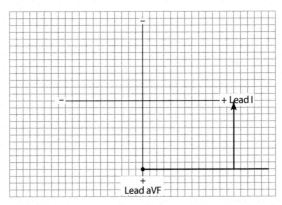

Figure 6.17 Perpendicular lines are drawn from each point. Where they intersect will determine the direction of the vector.

aVF, augmented vector foot.

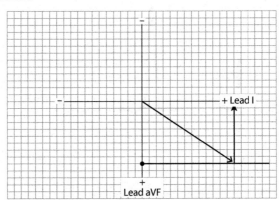

Figure 6.18 Because the vector always starts at the center (origin) of the graph, we can determine the vector's direction. When the vector runs in this quadrant, it is considered normal and is known as a normal axis deviation (NAD). It runs approximately in the same direction as the normal cardiac vector would run.

aVF, augmented vector foot.

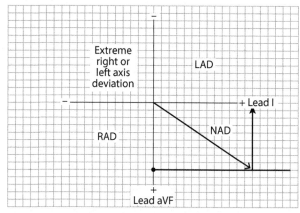

Figure 6.19 If the axis direction were in the upper-right corner of the graph, it would be considered a left axis deviation (LAD). If the vector ran through the lower-left quadrant, it would be considered a right axis deviation (RAD).

aVF, augmented vector foot; LAD, left axis deviation; NAD, normal axis deviation; RAD, right axis deviation.

EXAMPLE 1

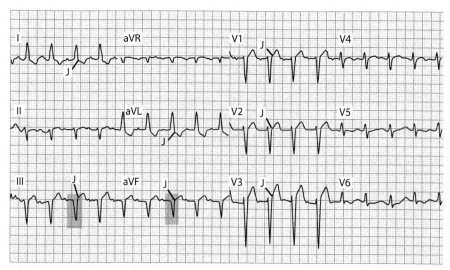

Figure 6.20 in Figure 6.20, the main complexes in lead I and lead aVF are going in opposite directions, but each has to be looked at individually.

aVF, augmented vector foot; aVL, augmented vector left; aVR, augmented vector right.

In the example shown in Figure 6.20, the main complexes in lead I and lead aVF are going in opposite directions, but each has to be looked at individually. In lead I, the J point is essentially isoelectric. That means no part of the QRS complex is negative (Figure 6.21).

Algebraically, +10 − 0 = 10. A dot should be placed on the lead I axis 10 squares from the origin (Figure 6.22).

Lead aVF is mostly negative by 10 squares, but does have some of the complex going positive (one square; Figure 6.23).

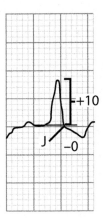

Figure 6.21 In lead I, the J point is essentially isoelectric. That means no part of the QRS complex is negative. Algebraically, +10 − 0 = 10.

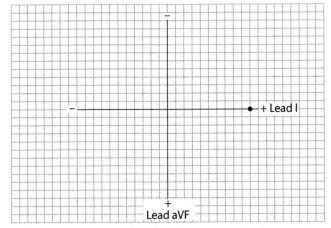

Figure 6.22 Algebraically, +10 − 0 = 10. A dot should be placed on the lead I axis 10 squares from the origin.

aVF, augmented vector foot.

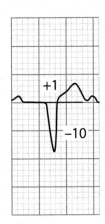

Figure 6.23 Lead aVF is mostly negative by 10 squares, but does have some of the complex going positive (one square above the isoelectric line). +10 −1 = 9.

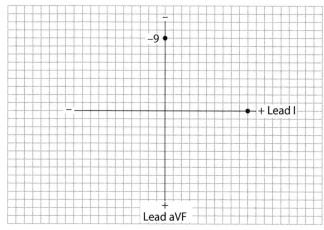

Figure 6.24 Algebraically, −10 + 1 = −9. A dot should be placed nine boxes from the origin. However, remember that this is a −9, and with aVF the negative pole is up.

aVF, augmented vector foot.

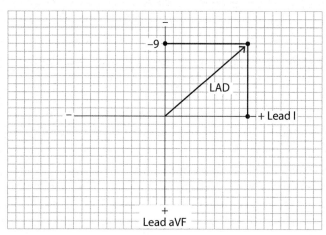

Figure 6.25 Once the perpendicular lines are drawn and the dots are connected, it will be easy to see that the EKG is showing a left axis deviation.

aVF, augmented vector foot; LAD, left axis deviation.

Algebraically, −10 + 1 = −9. A dot should be placed nine boxes from the origin. However, remember that this is a −9, and with aVF the negative pole is up. The dot should be placed as in Figure 6.24.

Once the perpendicular lines are drawn and the dots are connected, it will be easy to see that the EKG is showing a left axis deviation (Figure 6.25).

A left axis deviation is caused by either a loss of cells on the right side of the heart or an increase of cells on the left side. This EKG also shows Q waves in leads III and aVF, indicating an inferior wall MI. The inferior wall is nourished by the right coronary artery in most people, which would strengthen the argument that there was cell loss (death) on the right.

When reading the EKG, it is not simply a matter of recognizing the picture. It is a process. You must look for the presence of Q waves, ST elevation/depression, and T wave changes in each of the individual leads, and, then, determine the connection.

To this purpose, I have devised a grid that can be used to do exactly that. See Example 2 that follows.

In lead I, for example, the provider looks for Q waves. He or she also looks to see if the ST segment is isoelectric, elevated, or depressed. Next the T wave is observed to see if it is upright, flat, or inverted.

Once this is done, the same thing is done for lead II, then lead III, and all of the other leads. After all of the leads have been evaluated for these issues, then the leads are evaluated to see if any issues appear in related leads.

There is one problem with the 12 lead EKG. Each lead provides a very short sample of the heart rhythm which hampers its ability to detect many dysrhythmias. For that reason, there is usually a continuous long rhythm (usually lead II) at the bottom of the EKG to try gather that data.

Finally, axis deviation is determine utilizing leads I and aVF as described earlier.

EXAMPLE 2

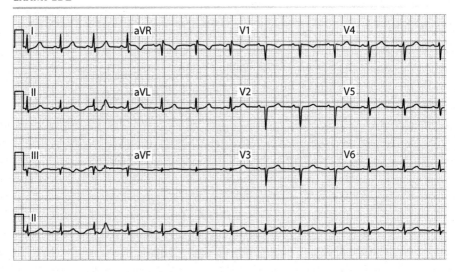

I	aVR	V1	V4
Q No	Q____	Q Yes	Q No
ST Isoelectric	ST____	ST Slightly elevated	ST Isoelectric
T Upright	T____	T Inverted	T Upright
II	aVL	V2	V5
Q No	Q No	Q Yes	Q No
ST Isoelectric	ST Isoelectric	ST Isoelectric	ST Isoelectric
T Upright	T Upright	T Upright	T Upright

III	aVF	V3	V6
Q Yes	Q Yes	Q No	Q No
ST Elevated	ST Isoelectric	ST Isoelectric	ST Isoelectric
T Inverted	T Inverted	T Upright	T Upright

- Axis: Normal axis
- Interpretation: There are significant Q waves in leads III and aVF, indicating an inferior wall MI. There is ST elevation in lead III, but aVF does not have ST elevation or depression so the age of the MI is uncertain. There are also significant Q waves in leads V1 and V2. This is suggestive of an anterior wall MI. There are very small R waves in V3, making the negative deflection an S wave. There is slight elevation of the ST segment in V1, but V2 has an isoelectric ST segment. Again, the age of the MI is uncertain. T waves are inverted in leads III and V1, but those leads are unrelated and so those changes mean nothing. This EKG should be compared with the patient's previous EKG to detect changes.
- Diagnosis: Inferior MI—age undetermined; anterior wall MI—age undetermined.

INTERPRETATION PRACTICE

Now it's your turn to practice. Remember that this is not rocket science. Take your time, and follow the steps. Also note that aVR is seldom used at our level, so do not worry about it.

EKG 6.1

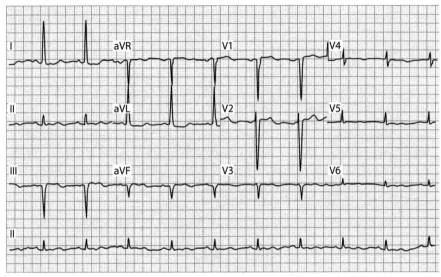

aVF, augmented vector foot; aVL, augmented vector left; aVR, augmented vector right; V, vector.

I	aVR	V1	V4
Q _____	Q _____	Q _____	Q _____
ST _____	ST _____	ST _____	ST _____
T _____	T _____	T _____	T _____
II	aVL	V2	V5
Q _____	Q _____	Q _____	Q _____
ST _____	ST _____	ST _____	ST _____
T _____	T _____	T _____	T _____
III	aVF	V3	V6
Q _____	Q _____	Q _____	Q _____
ST _____	ST _____	ST _____	ST _____
T _____	T _____	T _____	T _____

- Axis: _____

- Interpretation: _____

Answer on page 202

EKG 6.2

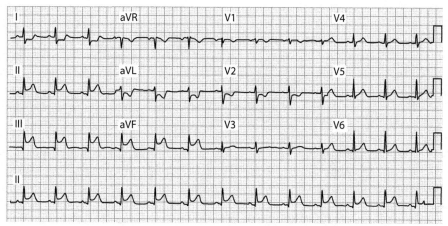

aVF, augmented vector foot; aVL, augmented vector left; aVR, augmented vector right; V, vector.

I	aVR	V1	V4
Q _____	Q _____	Q _____	Q _____
ST _____	ST _____	ST _____	ST _____
T _____	T _____	T _____	T _____
II	aVL	V2	V5
Q _____	Q _____	Q _____	Q _____
ST _____	ST _____	ST _____	ST _____
T _____	T _____	T _____	T _____
III	aVF	V3	V6
Q _____	Q _____	Q _____	Q _____
ST _____	ST _____	ST _____	ST _____
T _____	T _____	T _____	T _____

- Axis: _____

- Interpretation:_____

Answer on page 204

EKG 6.3

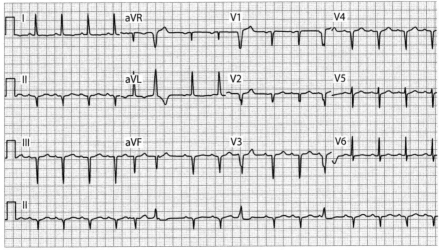

aVF, augmented vector foot; aVL, augmented vector left; aVR, augmented vector right; V, vector.

I	aVR	V1	V4
Q _____	Q _____	Q _____	Q _____
ST _____	ST _____	ST _____	ST _____
T _____	T _____	T _____	T _____
II	aVL	V2	V5
Q _____	Q _____	Q _____	Q _____
ST _____	ST _____	ST _____	ST _____
T _____	T _____	T _____	T _____
III	aVF	V3	V6
Q _____	Q _____	Q _____	Q _____
ST _____	ST _____	ST _____	ST _____
T _____	T _____	T _____	T _____

- Axis: _____

- Interpretation: _____

Answer on page 205

EKG 6.4

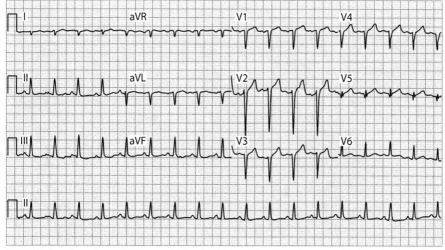

aVF, augmented vector foot; aVL, augmented vector left; aVR, augmented vector right; V, vector.

I	aVR	V1	V4
Q _____	Q _____	Q _____	Q _____
ST _____	ST _____	ST _____	ST _____
T _____	T _____	T _____	T _____
II	aVL	V2	V5
Q _____	Q _____	Q _____	Q _____
ST _____	ST _____	ST _____	ST _____
T _____	T _____	T _____	T _____
III	aVF	V3	V6
Q _____	Q _____	Q _____	Q _____
ST _____	ST _____	ST _____	ST _____
T _____	T _____	T _____	T _____

- Axis: _____

- Interpretation: _____

Answer on page 206

EKG 6.5

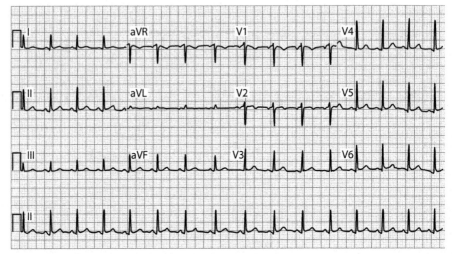

aVF, augmented vector foot; aVL, augmented vector left; aVR, augmented vector right; V, vector.

I	aVR	V1	V4
Q _____	Q _____	Q _____	Q _____
ST _____	ST _____	ST _____	ST _____
T _____	T _____	T _____	T _____
II	aVL	V2	V5
Q _____	Q _____	Q _____	Q _____
ST _____	ST _____	ST _____	ST _____
T _____	T _____	T _____	T _____
III	aVF	V3	V6
Q _____	Q _____	Q _____	Q _____
ST _____	ST _____	ST _____	ST _____
T _____	T _____	T _____	T _____

- Axis: _____

- Interpretation: _____

Answer on page 207

EKG 6.6

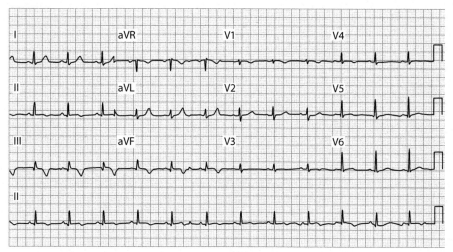

aVF, augmented vector foot; aVL, augmented vector left; aVR, augmented vector right; V, vector.

I	aVR	V1	V4
Q _____	Q _____	Q _____	Q _____
ST _____	ST _____	ST _____	ST _____
T _____	T _____	T _____	T _____
II	aVL	V2	V5
Q _____	Q _____	Q _____	Q _____
ST _____	ST _____	ST _____	ST _____
T _____	T _____	T _____	T _____
III	aVF	V3	V6
Q _____	Q _____	Q _____	Q _____
ST _____	ST _____	ST _____	ST _____
T _____	T _____	T _____	T _____

- Axis: _____

- Interpretation: _____

Answer on page 208

7

All Together Now!

Now you have all the rules and have had a chance to practice. In this chapter, you get to put it all together. Take your time and follow the rules, and remember that it takes practice to read an EKG. The more you do, the easier it will get. Now, go get 'em.

EKG 7.1

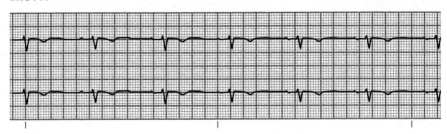

- Rate: Atrial _____ Ventricular _____

- Rhythm: Regular _____ Irregular _____

- P wave origin: _____

- PR interval: _____

- QRS: _____

- QT interval: _____

- Underlying rhythm: _____

- Variant: _____

- Interpretation: _____

- Treatment: _____

  _____

  _____

Answer on page 210

EKG 7.2

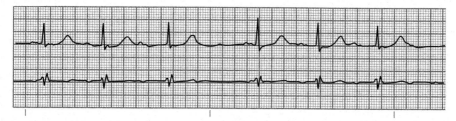

- Rate: Atrial _____ Ventricular _____
- Rhythm: Regular _____ Irregular _____
- P wave origin: _____
- PR interval: _____
- QRS: _____
- QT interval: _____
- Underlying rhythm: _____
- Variant: _____
- Interpretation: _____
- Treatment: _____

_____

_____

Answer on page 211

EKG 7.3

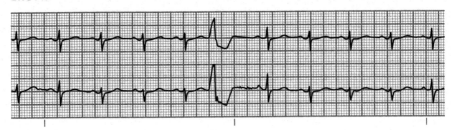

- Rate: Atrial _____ Ventricular _____

- Rhythm: Regular _____ Irregular _____

- P wave origin: _____

- PR interval: _____

- QRS: _____

- QT interval: _____

- Underlying rhythm: _____

- Variant: _____

- Interpretation: _____

- Treatment: _____

  _____

  _____

Answer on page 212

EKG 7.4

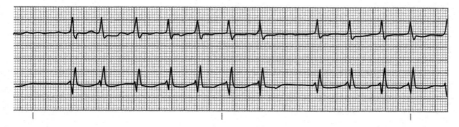

- Rate: Atrial _____ Ventricular _____
- Rhythm: Regular _____ Irregular _____
- P wave origin: _____
- PR interval: _____
- QRS: _____
- QT interval: _____
- Underlying rhythm: _____
- Variant: _____
- Interpretation: _____
- Treatment: _____
  _____
  _____

Answer on page 213

EKG 7.5

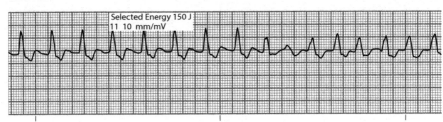

- Rate: Atrial _____ Ventricular _____
- Rhythm: Regular _____ Irregular _____
- P wave origin: _____
- PR interval: _____
- QRS: _____
- QT interval: _____
- Underlying rhythm: _____
- Variant: _____
- Interpretation: _____
- Treatment: _____

    _____

    _____

Answer on page 214

EKG 7.6

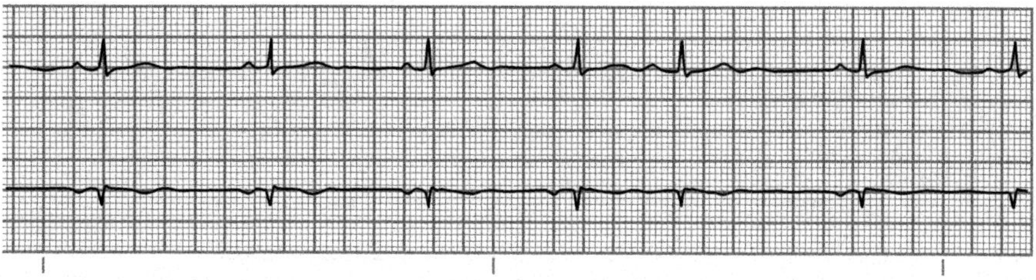

- Rate: Atrial _____ Ventricular _____
- Rhythm: Regular _____ Irregular _____
- P wave origin: _____
- PR interval: _____
- QRS: _____
- QT interval: _____
- Underlying rhythm: _____
- Variant: _____
- Interpretation: _____
- Treatment: _____

  _____

  _____

Answer on page 215

EKG 7.7

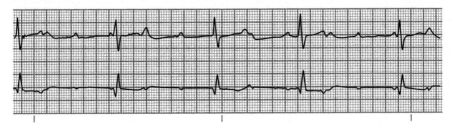

- Rate: Atrial _____ Ventricular _____

- Rhythm: Regular _____ Irregular _____

- P wave origin: _____

- PR interval: _____

- QRS: _____

- QT interval: _____

- Underlying rhythm: _____

- Variant: _____

- Interpretation: _____

- Treatment: _____

  _____

  _____

Answer on page 216

EKG 7.8

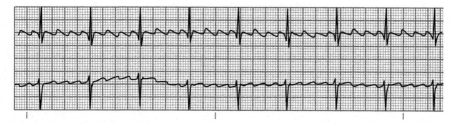

- Rate: Atrial _____ Ventricular _____
- Rhythm: Regular _____ Irregular _____
- P wave origin: _____
- PR interval: _____
- QRS: _____
- QT interval: _____
- Underlying rhythm: _____
- Variant: _____
- Interpretation: _____
- Treatment: _____

    _____

    _____

Answer on page 217

EKG 7.9

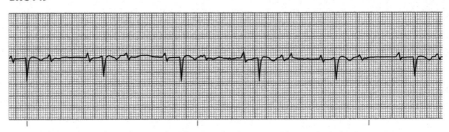

- Rate: Atrial _____ Ventricular _____

- Rhythm: Regular _____ Irregular _____

- P wave origin: _____

- PR interval: _____

- QRS: _____

- QT interval: _____

- Underlying rhythm: _____

- Variant: _____

- Interpretation: _____

- Treatment: _____

  _____

  _____

Answer on page 218

EKG 7.10

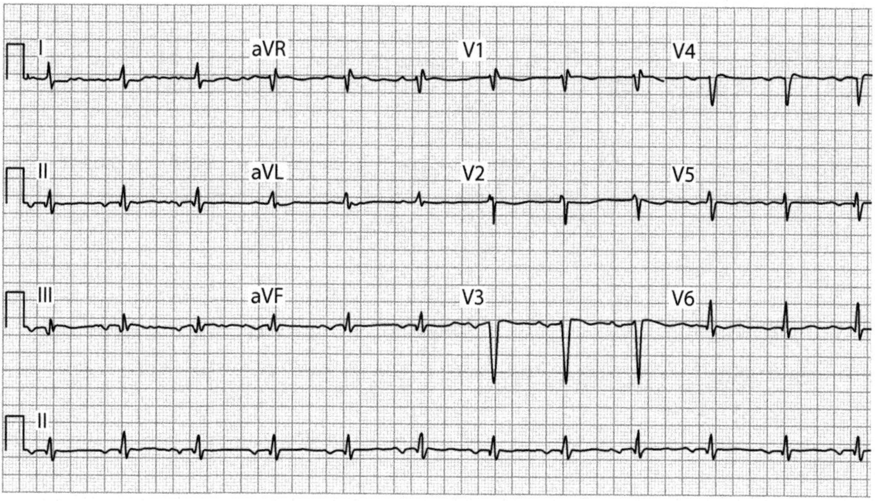

I	aVR	V1	V4
Q _____	Q _____	Q _____	Q _____
ST _____	ST _____	ST _____	ST _____
T _____	T _____	T _____	T _____
II	aVL	V2	V5
Q _____	Q _____	Q _____	Q _____
ST _____	ST _____	ST _____	ST _____
T _____	T _____	T _____	T _____
III	aVF	V3	V6
Q _____	Q _____	Q _____	Q _____
ST _____	ST _____	ST _____	ST _____
T _____	T _____	T _____	T _____

Axis: _____

Interpretation:_____

Answer on page 219

EKG 7.11

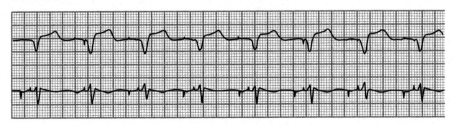

- Rate: Atrial _____ Ventricular _____

- Rhythm: Regular _____ Irregular _____

- P wave origin: _____

- PR interval: _____

- QRS: _____

- QT interval: _____

- Underlying rhythm: _____

- Variant: _____

- Interpretation: _____

- Treatment: _____

    _____

    _____

Answer on page 221

EKG 7.12

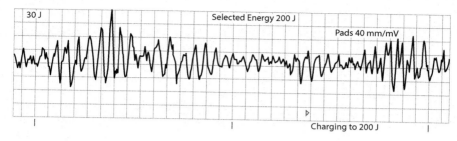

- Rate: Atrial _____ Ventricular _____
- Rhythm: Regular _____ Irregular _____
- P wave origin: _____
- PR interval: _____
- QRS: _____
- QT interval: _____
- Underlying rhythm: _____
- Variant: _____
- Interpretation: _____
- Treatment: _____

    _____

    _____

Answer on page 222

EKG 7.13

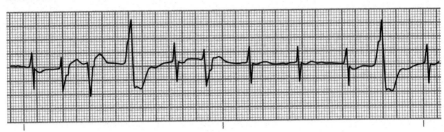

- Rate: Atrial _____ Ventricular _____

- Rhythm: Regular _____ Irregular _____

- P wave origin: _____

- PR interval: _____

- QRS: _____

- QT interval: _____

- Underlying rhythm: _____

- Variant: _____

- Interpretation: _____

- Treatment: _____

  _____

  _____

Answer on page 223

EKG 7.14

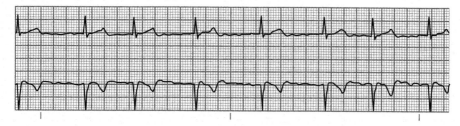

- Rate: Atrial _____ Ventricular _____
- Rhythm: Regular _____ Irregular _____
- P wave origin: _____
- PR interval: _____
- QRS: _____
- QT interval: _____
- Underlying rhythm: _____
- Variant: _____
- Interpretation: _____
- Treatment: _____

    _____

    _____

Answer on page 225

EKG 7.15

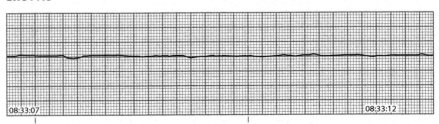

08:33:07   08:33:12

Source: Knechtel, M. (2017). *EKGs for nurse practitioners and physician assistants* (p. 176). New York, NY: Springer Publishing.

- Rate: Atrial _____ Ventricular _____
- Rhythm: Regular _____ Irregular _____
- P wave origin: _____
- PR interval: _____
- QRS: _____
- QT interval: _____
- Underlying rhythm: _____
- Variant: _____
- Interpretation: _____
- Treatment: _____

_____

_____

Answer on page 226

EKG 7.16

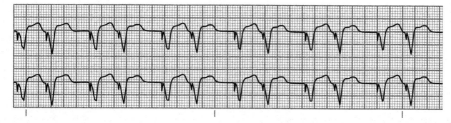

- Rate: Atrial _____ Ventricular _____
- Rhythm: Regular _____ Irregular _____
- P wave origin: _____
- PR interval: _____
- QRS: _____
- QT interval: _____
- Underlying rhythm: _____
- Variant: _____
- Interpretation: _____
- Treatment: _____

_____

_____

Answer on page 227

EKG 7.17

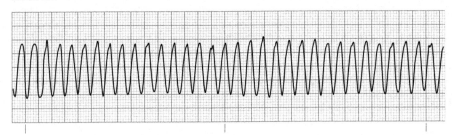

- Rate: Atrial _____ Ventricular _____
- Rhythm: Regular _____ Irregular _____
- P wave origin: _____
- PR interval: _____
- QRS: _____
- QT interval: _____
- Underlying rhythm: _____
- Variant: _____
- Interpretation: _____
- Treatment: _____

_____

_____

Answer on page 228

EKG 7.18

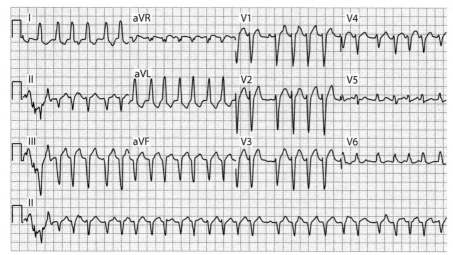

aVF, augmented vector foot; aVL, augmented vector left; aVR, augmented vector right; V, vector.

I	aVR	V1	V4
Q _____	Q _____	Q _____	Q _____
ST _____	ST _____	ST _____	ST _____
T _____	T _____	T _____	T _____
II	aVL	V2	V5
Q _____	Q _____	Q _____	Q _____
ST _____	ST _____	ST _____	ST _____
T _____	T _____	T _____	T _____
III	aVF	V3	V6
Q _____	Q _____	Q _____	Q _____
ST _____	ST _____	ST _____	ST _____
T _____	T _____	T _____	T _____

Axis: _____

Interpretation: _____

Answer on page 229

EKG 7.19

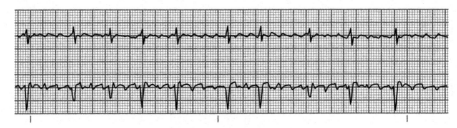

- Rate: Atrial _____ Ventricular _____

- Rhythm: Regular _____ Irregular _____

- P wave origin: _____

- PR interval: _____

- QRS: _____

- QT interval: _____

- Underlying rhythm: _____

- Variant: _____

- Interpretation: _____

- Treatment: _____

_____

_____

Answer on page 230

EKG 7.20

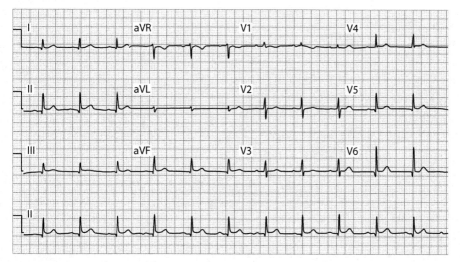

aVF, augmented vector foot; aVL, augmented vector left; aVR, augmented vector right; V, vector.

I	aVR	V1	V4
Q _____	Q _____	Q _____	Q _____
ST _____	ST _____	ST _____	ST _____
T _____	T _____	T _____	T _____
II	aVL	V2	V5
Q _____	Q _____	Q _____	Q _____
ST _____	ST _____	ST _____	ST _____
T _____	T _____	T _____	T _____
III	aVF	V3	V6
Q _____	Q _____	Q _____	Q _____
ST _____	ST _____	ST _____	ST _____
T _____	T _____	T _____	T _____

Axis: _____

Interpretation: _____

Answer on page 231

EKG 7.21

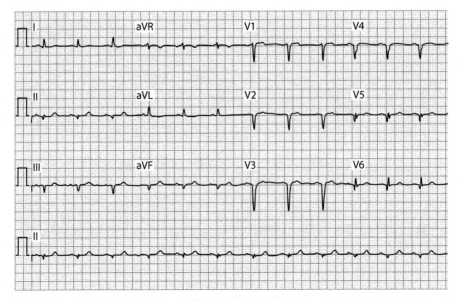

aVF, augmented vector foot; aVL, augmented vector left; aVR, augmented vector right; V, vector.

I	aVR	V1	V4
Q _____	Q _____	Q _____	Q _____
ST _____	ST _____	ST _____	ST _____
T _____	T _____	T _____	T _____
II	aVL	V2	V5
Q _____	Q _____	Q _____	Q _____
ST _____	ST _____	ST _____	ST _____
T _____	T _____	T _____	T _____
III	aVF	V3	V6
Q _____	Q _____	Q _____	Q _____
ST _____	ST _____	ST _____	ST _____
T _____	T _____	T _____	T _____

Axis: _____

Interpretation: _____

Answer on page 233

EKG 7.22

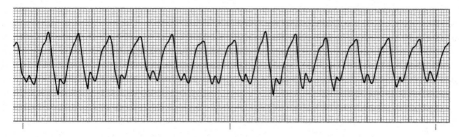

- Rate: Atrial _____ Ventricular _____
- Rhythm: Regular _____ Irregular _____
- P wave origin: _____
- PR interval: _____
- QRS: _____
- QT interval: _____
- Underlying rhythm: _____
- Variant: _____
- Interpretation: _____
- Treatment: _____
    _____
    _____

Answer on page 234

EKG 7.23

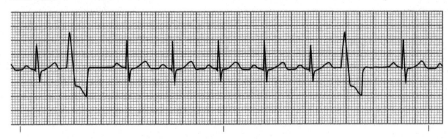

- Rate: Atrial _____ Ventricular _____

- Rhythm: Regular _____ Irregular _____

- P wave origin: _____

- PR interval: _____

- QRS: _____

- QT interval: _____

- Underlying rhythm: _____

- Variant: _____

- Interpretation: _____

- Treatment: _____

  _____

  _____

Answer on page 235

EKG 7.24

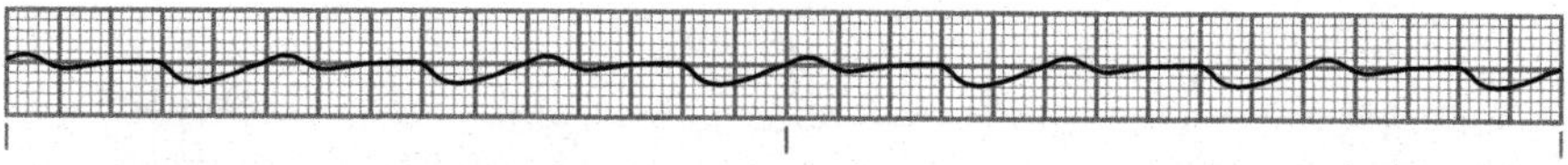

Source: Landrum, M. A. (2014). *Fast facts about EKGs for nurses: The rules of identifying EKGs in a nutshell* (p. 100). New York, NY: Springer Publishing.

- Rate: Atrial _____ Ventricular _____
- Rhythm: Regular _____ Irregular _____
- P wave origin: _____
- PR interval: _____
- QRS: _____
- QT interval: _____
- Underlying rhythm: _____
- Variant: _____
- Interpretation: _____
- Treatment: _____

_____

_____

Answer on page 236

EKG 7.25

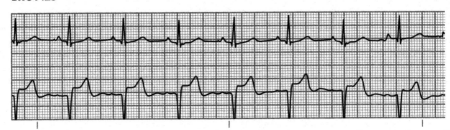

- Rate: Atrial _____ Ventricular _____

- Rhythm: Regular _____ Irregular _____

- P wave origin: _____

- PR interval: _____

- QRS: _____

- QT interval: _____

- Underlying rhythm: _____

- Variant: _____

- Interpretation: _____

- Treatment: _____

  _____

  _____

Answer on page 238

II

Answers

Answers to Chapter 1: Atrial Rhythms

EKG 1.1

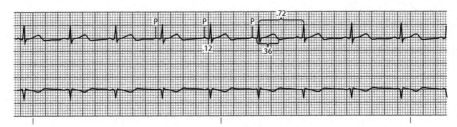

- Rate: Atrial <u>80 beats per minute (bpm)</u> Ventricular <u>80 bpm</u>

- Rhythm: Regular

- P wave origin: <u>SA node</u>

- PR interval: <u>0.12 seconds</u>

- QRS: <u>0.08 seconds</u>

- QT interval: <u>0.36 seconds (R-R interval = 0.72 seconds)</u>

- Underlying rhythm: <u>Sinus rhythm</u>

- Variant: <u>None</u>

- Diagnosis: <u>Normal sinus rhythm</u>

- Treatment: <u>None</u>

- Discussion

    - **Rate:** There are eight P waves in the 6-second strip (between the first and third 3-second marker): $8 \times 10 = 80$ P waves per minute. There are also eight QRS complexes between those markers, giving a ventricular rate of 80 bpm (beats per minute).

    - **Rhythm:** The interval between the R waves is consistent, meaning that the rhythm is regular.

    - **P wave origin:** Because the P waves all look the same, they are most likely coming from the same place and going through the same tissue. The assumption is that place of origin is the sinoatrial (SA) node. This will be a "sinus something."

    - **PR interval:** The PR interval is consistently three little blocks wide. Each block is 0.04 seconds wide so the PR width is consistently 0.12 seconds. That is within the normal range (0.10–0.20 seconds).

    - **QRS:** The QRS complexes all look the same and are 0.08 seconds (two blocks) wide, making them normal in configuration.

    - **QT interval:** The QT interval is exactly one half the R-R interval. One half or less is acceptable. Greater than one half the R-R interval may place the patient at risk for arrhythmia.

    - **Underlying rhythm:** The P wave is sinus in origin. The rate is within normal limits and the rhythm is regular. This is a normal sinus rhythm. There are no variations noted.

EKG 1.2

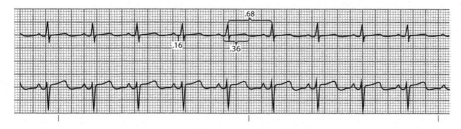

- Rate: Atrial <u>80 bpm</u> Ventricular <u>80 bpm</u>
- Rhythm: Regular
- P wave origin: <u>SA node</u>
- PR interval: <u>0.16 seconds</u>
- QRS: <u>0.08 seconds</u>
- QT interval: <u>0.36 seconds (R-R interval = 0.68 seconds)</u>
- Underlying rhythm: <u>Sinus rhythm</u>
- Variant: <u>QT greater than one half of R-R interval</u>
- Diagnosis: <u>Normal sinus rhythm</u>
- Treatment: <u>None. Watch QT interval and evaluate causes and risk.</u>
- Discussion
    - **Rate:** There are eight P waves and eight QRS complexes between the first and third 3-second marker (6 seconds), giving a rate of 80 bpm.
    - **Rhythm:** The R-R interval is consistent, indicating that the rhythm is regular.
    - **P wave origin:** All the P waves look the same, indicating that they are all coming from the same place. That same place is assumed to be the SA node.
    - **PR interval:** The PR interval is consistent at 0.16 seconds (four boxes). That is an acceptable width (0.10–0.20 seconds).
    - **QRS:** The QRS is narrow (<0.12 seconds wide) and consistent in appearance.
    - **QT interval:** The QT interval is a tad more than one half the R-R interval and bears watching for progression and the development of premature beats.

EKG 1.3

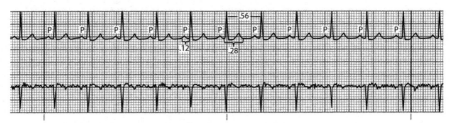

- Rate: Atrial <u>110 bpm</u> Ventricular <u>110 bpm</u>
- Rhythm: Regular
- P wave origin: <u>SA node</u>
- PR interval: <u>0.12 seconds</u>
- QRS: <u>0.08 seconds</u>
- QT interval: <u>0.28 seconds (R-R interval = 0.56 seconds)</u>
- Underlying rhythm: <u>Sinus</u>
- Variant: <u>Rapid rate</u>
- Diagnosis: <u>Sinus tachycardia</u>
- Treatment: <u>Treatment begins by determining and alleviating the cause of the tachcardia (Bucher, 2014; Marcum, 2013). Pain medication or antipyretics can be used if the tachycardia is secondary to pain or fever (marcum, 2013). If that does not work, medications, such as beta-adrenergic blockers (propranolol, metoprolol, etc.), calcium channel blockers (cardizem, diltiazem, etc.), or adenosine (Adenocard), may be effective (Bucher, 2014). As a last resort, electrocardioversion (electric shock) may be used (Bucher, 2014), but only if the patient is rapidly decompensating.</u>
- Discussion
  - **Rate:** There are 11 P waves and QRS complexes between the first and third 3-second marker (6 seconds), indicating an atrial and ventricular rate of 110 bpm.
  - **Rhythm:** The rhythm is regular.
  - **P wave origin:** All the P waves are consistent, indicating that they are probably coming from the SA node.
  - **PR interval:** The PR is consistent at 0.12 seconds wide.
  - **QRS:** The QRS complexes are consistent and 0.08 seconds wide.
  - **QT interval:** The QT interval is one half the R-R interval and bears watching for progression and the development of arrhythmias.
  - **Diagnosis:** The origin of this rhythm is the SA node, but the rate is rapid (>100 bpm), making this a sinus tachycardia.

EKG 1.4

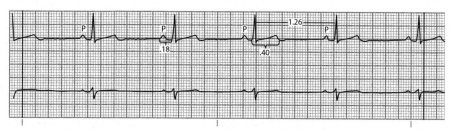

- Rate: Atrial 50 bpm Ventricular 50 bpm
- Rhythm: Regular
- P wave origin: SA node
- PR interval: 0.18 seconds
- QRS: 0.08 seconds
- QT interval: 0.40 seconds (R-R interval = 1.26 seconds)
- Underlying rhythm: Sinus
- Variant: Bradycardia
- Diagnosis: Sinus bradycardia
- Treatment: Assess the patient. The treatment in this case would depend on whether or not the patient is symptomatic. If not, leave him or her alone. He or she may be sleeping comfortably, dreaming about how he or she won that gold medal. Don't take that away from him or her. If, however, the patient is complaining of chest discomfort, shortness of breath, and so on, atropine would be the drug of choice. If atropine is not effective, epinephrine or dopamine might be used. If none of the medications work, apply the transcutaneous pacemaker.
- Discussion
  - **Rate:** There are five P waves and five QRS complexes between the first and third 3-second marker (6 seconds) of this strip, making the atrial and ventricular rates 50 bpm.
  - **Rhythm:** The R-R intervals are consistent, making the rhythm regular.
  - **P wave origin:** All the P waves look the same, indicating that they are coming from the same place and going through the same pathway. The assumption is that the source of the P waves is the sinoatrial (SA) node.
  - **PR interval:** The PR interval is within the normal limits (0.10–0.20 seconds).
  - **QRS:** The QRS complexes all look the same and are within normal limits (<0.12 seconds).
  - **QT interval:** The QT interval is less than one half the R-R interval.
  - **Diagnosis:** The source of this rhythm is the SA node, but the rate is slow (<60 bpm), making this a sinus bradycardia.

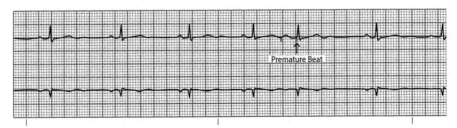

EKG 1.5

Premature Beat

- Rate: Atrial 60 bpm Ventricular 60 bpm
- Rhythm: Irregular due to beat #5 being early
- P wave origin: SA node (beat #5 is atrial)
- PR interval: 0.16 seconds (beat #5 = 0.24)
- QRS: 0.08 seconds
- QT interval: 0.40 seconds (R-R interval = 1.28 seconds)
- Underlying rhythm: Sinus rhythm
- Variant: Premature atrial contraction
- Diagnosis: Sinus rhythm with premature atrial contractions
- Treatment: Premature atrial contractions are not that uncommon. Therefore, if there are fewer than six per minute, they are not usually treated (Bucher, 2014; Diehl, 2011). If there are more than six per minute, they may be a sign that worse things are to come, such as atrial tachycardia, atrial flutter, or atrial fibrillation. If at all possible, treat the cause (Bucher, 2014; Diehl, 2011). If this is not possible, or not effective, beta-blockers are the preferred medication in the treatment of premature atrial contractions (Bucher, 2014).
- Discussion
  - **Rate:** There are six P waves and six QRS complexes, making the atrial and ventricular rate 60 bpm each.
  - **Rhythm:** Beat number five comes early, creating an irregular rhythm.
  - **P wave origin:** All the P waves look alike, except for the P wave that begins beat number five. That P wave looks different than the others so it must be coming from someplace other than the sinoatrial node.Because all P waves come from the atria, beat number five is an atrial beat, whereas all the others are assumed to arise from the sinoatrial node.
  - **PR interval:** The P waves assumed to be sinus in origin have consistent PR intervals of 0.16 seconds. Beat number five has a PR interval of 0.24, further strengthening the argument that its origin is from some atrial focus other than the sinoatrial node.
  - **QRS:** All the QRS complexes look the same and are of normal size. Because of this, conduction through the ventricles can be assumed to be normal.
  - **QT interval:** The QT interval is less than one half the R-R interval.
  - **Diagnosis:** The origin of most of this rhythm is the sinoatrial node. The rate is normal, but there is a variant beat. That beat is coming early and from the atria. This is a sinus rhythm with a premature atrial contraction.

EKG 1.6

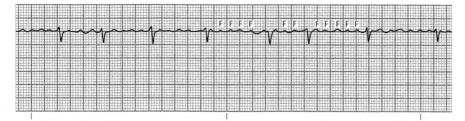

- Rate: Atrial >200 bpm Ventricular 70 bpm
- Rhythm: Irregular
- P wave origin: Atrial F waves
- PR interval: Not applicable
- QRS: 0.10 seconds
- QT interval: Not applicable
- Underlying rhythm: Atrial flutter
- Variant: F waves
- Diagnosis: Atrial flutter (controlled)
- Treatment: The primary goal is to convert the atrial flutter back to a sinus rhythm. This can be done by way of electrical cardioversion or by the use of medications such as ibutilide (Corvert; Bucher, 2014; Marcum, 2013). Once converted, medications, such as amiodarone, flecainide (Tambocor), or dronedarone (Multaq), are used to maintain sinus rhythm (Bucher, 2014). If this cannot be done, rate control is needed to improve cardiac function. This can be done using calcium channel blockers or beta-adrenergic blockers (Bucher, 2014). Anticoagulation may be needed to reduce the risk of thromboembolism (Diehl, 2011).
- Discussion
  - **Rate:** The atrial rate is very rapid and difficult to count. There are lots and lots of P waves. However, each person is only allowed one P wave per QRS complex. If there are more, as in this strip, they are not P waves but F waves, or flutter waves, and your diagnosis is made. The ventricular rate, however, is extremely important. There are seven QRS complexes between the first and third 3-second marker, so the ventricular rate is 70 bpm. Because the atrial rate is so rapid, atrial filling time is reduced, so less blood is in the atria for pumping. This leads to a loss of cardiac output. In order to maximize cardiac output, it is important to keep the ventricular rate in a normal range to maximize ventricular filling. We must "control" the ventricular rate.

EKG 1.7

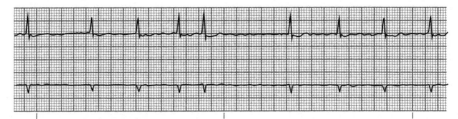

- Rate: Atrial <u>0</u> Ventricular <u>70 bpm</u>

- Rhythm: <u>Irregular</u>

- P wave origin: <u>Not applicable</u>

- PR interval: <u>Not applicable</u>

- QRS: <u>0.08 seconds</u>

- QT interval: <u>Not applicable</u>

- Underlying rhythm: <u>Atrial fibrillation</u>

- Variant: <u>No p wave; irregular rhythm</u>

- Diagnosis: <u>Atrial fibrillation</u>

- Treatment: <u>The main goal of treatment is to convert the atrial fibrillation back to a normal sinus rhythm. The problem is that atrial fibrillation is not a disease. It is a symptom. Something has caused this to happen. In order to prevent the atrial fibrillation from reoccurring, the cause must be determined and dealt with. Sometimes the cause is known, but then nothing can be done to treat it. Atrial fibrillation is extremely common in people who have lung diseases such as chronic obstructive pulmonary disease (COPD). However, the damage done by smoking is not reversible, so there is little that can be done to cure the COPD, limiting treatment options for the fibrillation. There is concern about converting the patient back to normal sinus rhythm. The atria are full of blood clots that are stable in the noncontracting atria. Once the atria begin to contract, these blood clots will be released. In this case, the cure may be worse than the disease. For this reason, transesophageal echocardiograms may be done to determine the presence of blood clots in the atria. If they are present, the patient may be treated with an anticoagulant, usually heparin or warfarin (although some newer medications are now available, such as dabigatran [Pradaxa], apixaban [Eliquis], and rivaroxaban [Xarelto]), until the body reabsorbs the blood clots (Bucher, 2014). Once it has been determined that the patient is free of blood clots in the atria, conversion can be attempted. This can be done chemically, with medications such as amiodarone or ibutilide (Bucher, 2014), or electrically using synchronized cardioversion (Bucher, 2014).</u>

<u>In some patients, cardioversions are short lived or not effective. For these people, rate control is of prime importance in order to maximize cardiac output. When heart rate is greater than 100 bpm or less than 60 bpm, the fibrillation is considered to be uncontrolled. Atrial fibrillation is considered "controlled" when the rate is between 60 and 100 bpm. This can be attained by using calcium channel blockers such as diltiazem, beta-adrenergic blockers such as metoprolol, or digoxin</u>

(Bucher, 2014). However, digoxin levels should be obtained before digoxin is given and while the patient is on the drug to prevent the formation of lethal arrhythmias secondary to digoxin toxicity (Diehl, 2011).

- Discussion: The more lethal the dysrhythmia, the easier it is to detect. That is proof of God. He has made it easier to detect and save lives and easier to interpret so that students have an easier time passing cardiology exams. What could be more divine than that? Atrial fibrillation, by definition, is an irregular rhythm that has no P waves. There is no atrial rate here and the rhythm is irregular. The diagnosis is atrial fibrillation. The risks include a much higher potential for embolic events such as stroke and pulmonary embolism.

EKG 1.8

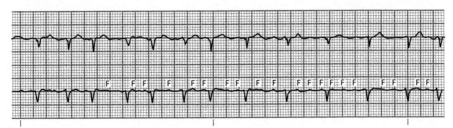

- Rate: Atrial <u>>200 bpm</u> Ventricular <u>110 bpm</u>
- Rhythm: Irregular
- P wave origin: <u>Atrial flutter waves</u>
- PR interval: <u>Not applicable</u>
- QRS: <u>0.08 seconds</u>
- QT interval: <u>Not applicable</u>
- Underlying rhythm: <u>Atrial flutter</u>
- Variant: <u>Flutter waves</u>
- Diagnosis: <u>Atrial flutter (uncontrolled)</u>
- Treatment: <u>The primary goal is to convert the atrial flutter back to a sinus rhythm. This can be done by way of electrical cardioversion or by the use of medications such as ibutilide (Corvert; Bucher, 2014; Marcum, 2013). Once converted, medications, such as amiodarone, flecanide (Tambocor), or dronedarone (Multaq), are used to maintain sinus rhythm (Bucher, 2014). If this cannot be done, rate control is needed to improve cardiac function. This can be done using calcium channel blockers or beta-adrenergic blockers (Bucher, 2014). Anticoagulation may be needed to reduce the risk of thromboembolism (Diehl, 2011).</u>
- Discussion: This strip demonstrates the beauty of having two leads on one piece of paper. If there was only the top rhythm, it would be diagnosed as atrial fibrillation. It is certainly irregular, and there are not any P waves. However, in the second lead, the F waves are clearly visible, making this atrial flutter. Just to show that even the best can be fooled at times.

EKG 1.9

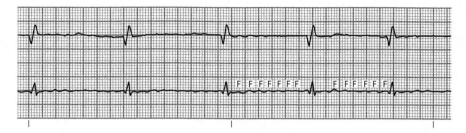

- Rate: Atrial >200 bpm Ventricular 50 bpm

- Rhythm: Irregular

- P wave origin: Atrial flutter waves

- PR interval: Not applicable

- QRS: 0.12 seconds

- QT interval: Not applicable

- Underlying rhythm: Atrial flutter

- Variant: Flutter waves

- Diagnosis: Atrial flutter (uncontrolled)

- Treatment: The primary goal is to convert the atrial flutter back to a sinus rhythm. This can be done by way of electrical cardioversion or by the use of medications such as ibutilide (Corvert; Bucher, 2014; Marcum, 2013). Once converted, medications, such as amiodarone, flecanide (Tambocor), or dronedarone (Multaq), are used to maintain sinus rhythm (Bucher, 2014). If this cannot be done, rate control is needed to improve cardiac function. This can be done using calcium channel blockers or beta-adrenergic blockers (Bucher, 2014). Anticoagulation may be needed to reduce the risk of thromboembolism (Diehl, 2011).

- Discussion: Just as in EKG 1.8, this strip demonstrates the beauty of having two leads on one piece of paper. If there is only the top rhythm, it would be diagnosed as atrial fibrillation. It is certainly irregular, and there are not any P waves. However, in the second lead, the F waves are clearly visible, making this atrial flutter.

EKG 1.10

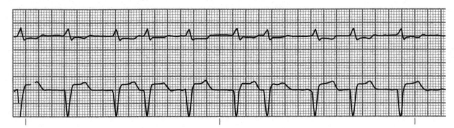

- Rate: Atrial <u>0</u> Ventricular <u>90 bpm</u>

- Rhythm: Irregular

- P wave origin: <u>Not applicable</u>

- PR interval: <u>Not applicable</u>

- QRS: <u>0.12 seconds</u>

- QT interval: <u>Not applicable</u>

- Underlying rhythm: <u>Atrial fibrillation</u>

- Variant: <u>No P waves; irregular rhythm</u>

- Diagnosis: <u>Atrial fibrillation (controlled)</u>

- Treatment: <u>The main goal of treatment is to convert the atrial fibrillation back
  to a normal sinus rhythm. The problem is that atrial fibrillation is not a disease.
  It is a symptom. Something has caused this to happen. In order to prevent the
  atrial fibrillation from reoccurring, the cause must be determined and dealt with.
  Sometimes the cause is known, but then nothing can be done to treat it. Atrial
  fibrillation is extremely common in people who have lung diseases such as COPD.
  However, the damage done by smoking is not reversible, so there is little that can
  be done to cure the COPD, limiting treatment options for the fibrillation. There is
  concern about converting the patient back to normal sinus rhythm. The atria are
  full of blood clots that are stable in the noncontracting atria. Once the atria begin
  to contract, those blood clots will be released. In this case, the cure may be worse
  than the disease. For this reason, transesophageal echocardiograms may be done to
  determine the presence of blood clots in the atria. If they are present, the patient may
  be treated with an anticoagulant, usually heparin or warfarin (although some newer
  medications are now available such as dabigatran [Pradaxa], apixaban [Eliquis],
  and rivaroxaban [Xaralto]), until the body reabsorbs these blood clots (Bucher,
  2014). Once it has been determined that the patient is free of blood clots in the
  atria, conversion can be attempted. This can be done chemically, with medications
  such as amiodarone or ibutilide (Bucher, 2014), or electrically using synchronized
  cardioversion (Bucher, 2014).</u>
  <u>In some patients, cardioversions are short lived or not effective. For these
  people, rate control is of prime importance in order to maximize cardiac output.
  When heart rate is greater than 100 bpm or less than 60 bpm, the fibrillation is
  considered to be uncontrolled. Atrial fibrillation is considered "controlled" when the
  rate is between 60 and 100 bpm. This can be attained by using calcium channel</u>

blockers such as diltiazem, beta-adrenergic blockers such as metoprolol, or digoxin (Bucher, 2014). However, digoxin levels should be obtained before digoxin is given and while the patient is on it to prevent the formation of lethal arrhythmias secondary to digoxin toxicity (Diehl, 2011).

- **Discussion:** There are no P waves and the rhythm is irregular. By definition, this is atrial fibrillation. However, the rate is between 60 and 100 bpm; therefore it is considered to be controlled in order to maximize cardiac output.

Answers to Chapter 2: Junctional Rhythms

EKG 2.1

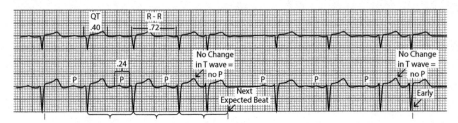

- Rate: Atrial <u>60 beats per minute (bpm)</u> Ventricular <u>80 bpm</u>

- Rhythm: Irregular, since beats 5 and 9 come early

- P wave origin: <u>SA node</u>

- PR interval: <u>0.24 seconds</u>

- QRS: <u>0.12 seconds</u>

- QT interval: <u>0.40 seconds (R-R interval = 0.72 seconds)</u>

- Underlying rhythm: <u>Sinus rhythm</u>

- Variant: <u>Beats 5 and 9 have no P waves</u>

- Interpretation: <u>Sinus rhythm with first-degree atrioventricular (AV) block and premature junctional beats (PJCs)</u>

- Treatment: <u>Assess the patient and attempt to determine the cause and remove it. Digitalis is a common treatment, but as digitalis toxicity may be a cause, a digoxin level should be obtained prior to administration if the patient has been on it at home (Bucher, 2014, Diehl, 2011). Other medications that can be used are calcium channel blockers, beta-adrenergic blockers, and amiodarone (Bucher, 2014).</u>

- Discussion

  - **Rate:** The ventricular rate is greater than the atrial rate. This means that P waves are missing. Sometimes the P waves are obscured by the preceding T waves. The Ps and the Ts bump into each other. It's never good to have P in your T. It always causes T wave distortion. In this case, there is no T wave distortion. All the T waves look the same; therefore, the assumption is that there are no P waves in them. Because beats 5 and 9 have no P waves, they cannot be originating from the atria.

  - **Rhythm:** The rhythm is irregular because beats 5 and 9 happen before the next expected beat. That makes them "premature." So beats 5 and 9 are premature beats that are not coming from the atria.

  - **P wave origin:** The P waves that are present all look the same, indicating a common focus of origin. The assumption is that the focus is the SA node.

  - **PR interval:** When present, the PR interval is consistent at 0.24 seconds. That is longer than usual (0.10–0.20 is considered normal) and indicates the presence of first-degree block.

- **QRS:** The QRS complexes all look the same, indicating that the conduction from the junction through the ventricles is normal. Even the QRS complexes for beats 5 and 9 look like the other QRS complexes, indicating that the point of origin for these beats is not ventricular but junctional.
- **QT interval:** The QT interval is more than one half the R-R interval and should be watched.

EKG 2.2

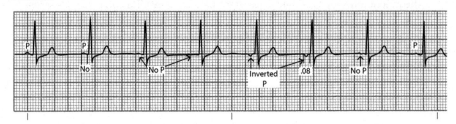

- Rate: Atrial <u>60 bpm</u> Ventricular <u>80 bpm</u>

- Rhythm: Regular

- P wave origin: <u>Junction</u>

- PR interval: <u>Less than 0.10 seconds</u>

- QRS: <u>0.08 seconds</u>

- QT interval: <u>0.32 seconds (R-R interval = 0.80 seconds)</u>

- Underlying rhythm: <u>Junctional rhythm</u>

- Variant: <u>Variable focus in junction</u>

- Interpretation: <u>Junctional rhythm</u>

- Treatment: <u>This is an interesting rhythm in that some complexes have P waves and some do not. Some of the P waves are upside down, possibly indicating retrograde (backward) conduction. However, when there are PR intervals, they are less than 0.10 seconds. This rhythm is arising from the junction, but the different P wave configurations and the absence of P waves may indicate that it may be coming from different parts of the junction. The overall rate is good, so a "wait and see" attitude may be justified while evaluating possible causes. At any rate, this is not a rhythm that you want to stop. This is a rhythm that you want to replace. The part of the heart that supersedes the AV node is the SA node, so the treatment of this rhythm is to kick-start the SA node. This should be treated as if it were a sinus bradycardia. Atropine is the drug of choice, followed by dopamine or epinephrine. If you get the SA node working at a rate faster than the AV node, it will regain control of the rhythm (Diehl, 2011). However, as long as the junctional rate is fast enough, and the patient is asymptomatic, this could be a rhythm to be watched in the hope that it will be self-limiting and the SA node will take over again. Prepare for possible pacemaker application (Diehl, 2011).</u>

- Discussion

  - **Rate and rhythm:** There are more QRS complexes than P waves. However, the rhythm is regular, ruling out any "premature" or escape (late) beats.
  - **P waves:** The P waves are inconsistent. The P waves in beats 1, 2, and 8 look the same and are probably coming from the same place in the atria. Beats 3, 4, and 7 have no P waves, while beats 5 and 6 have P waves that are upside down. The variability in P wave configuration indicates multiple origins for these beats.

- **PR interval and QRS:** The PR intervals, when present, are all less than 0.10 seconds, indicating that beats 1, 2, 5, and 6 are junctional in origin albeit from two different areas in the junction. Beats 3, 4, and 7 have no P waves, but the QRS complexes look like all the others and are narrow in configuration, indicating that those beats are also arising from the junction but from a third focus in the junction.

EKG 2.3

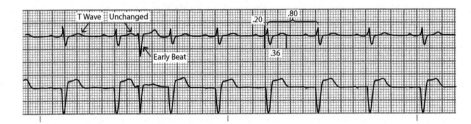

- Rate: Atrial <u>80 bpm</u> Ventricular <u>90 bpm</u>

- Rhythm: Irregular

- P wave origin: <u>SA node</u>

- PR interval: <u>0.20 seconds</u>

- QRS: <u>0.12 seconds</u>

- QT interval: <u>0.36 seconds (R-R interval = 0.80 seconds)</u>

- Underlying rhythm: <u>Sinus rhythm</u>

- Variant: <u>Beat number 3 is early and has no P wave (PJC)</u>

- Interpretation: <u>Sinus rhythm with premature junctional beats</u>

- Treatment: <u>Assess the patient and attempt to determine the cause and remove it.
  If infrequent, there is no treatment. If frequent, digitalis is a common treatment, but
  since digitalis toxicity may be a cause of this irregularity, a digoxin level should be
  obtained prior to administration if the patient has been on it at home (Bucher, 2014;
  Diehl, 2011). Other medications that can be used are calcium channel blockers, beta-
  adrenergic blockers, and amiodarone (Bucher, 2014).</u>

- Discussion

  - **Rate and rhythm:** The ventricular rate is greater than the atrial rate, and the
    rhythm is irregular due to beat number 3 being early (premature).
  - **P wave origin:** When the P waves are present, they are consistent in configuration,
    indicating that they are originating from the same place. That place is assumed to
    be the SA node. Beat number 3, however, has no P wave. Sometimes, however, if
    the premature beat is early enough, the T wave can "bump" into the P wave and
    hide it. Notice how the T wave of the beat immediately preceding the PJC looks
    the same as the other T waves in the rhythm. If it were distorted, it could be said
    that something was in the T wave causing the distortion. The only thing that
    would be between the T wave and the next QRS would be a P wave. Because there
    is no distortion of the T wave, the assumption is that there is no P wave in the
    location to cause distortion.
  - **QRS:** The QRS complexes all look the same except for beat number 3, but all are
    within normal limits, indicating that beat number 3 is not ventricular in origin.
    Because there is no P wave for beat number 3, it is not atrial or sinus in origin
    either. That leaves only the junction.

EKG 2.4

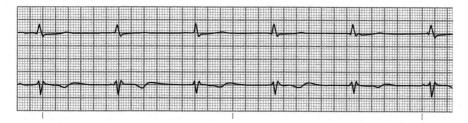

- Rate: Atrial 0 Ventricular 40 bpm

- Rhythm: Regular

- P wave origin: None

- PR interval: Not applicable

- QRS: 0.12 seconds

- QT interval: 0.52 seconds (R-R interval = 1.24 seconds)

- Underlying rhythm: Junctional

- Variant: Not applicable

- Interpretation: Junctional rhythm

- Treatment: If the patient is asymptomatic, watch the rhythm. If symptomatic, give atropine, dopamine, or epinephrine. Possible pacemaker.

- Discussion

  - **Rate:** There are no P waves, so there is no atrial rate. The ventricular rate of 40 suggests a junctional origin because the "normal" rate for the junction is 40 to 60 bpm. Because there are no P waves, there are no PR intervals.
  - **Rhythm:** The lack of P waves would make one think of atrial fibrillation (A-fib). However, this rhythm is regular, and one of the hallmarks of A-fib is its irregular rhythm. This is not A-fib.
  - **QRS:** The QRS complexes are all consistent in configuration and within normal limits, indicating normal conduction through the ventricles.

EKG 2.5

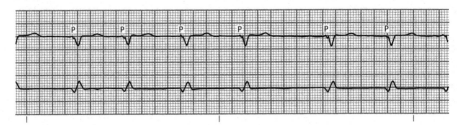

- Rate: Atrial <u>60 bpm</u> (see top rhythm) Ventricular <u>60 bpm</u>
- Rhythm: Irregular
- P wave origin: <u>Junction</u>
- PR interval: <u>0.08 seconds</u>
- QRS: <u>0.16 seconds</u>
- QT interval: <u>0.44 seconds (R-R interval = 0.90 seconds)</u>
- Underlying rhythm: <u>Junctional</u>
- Variant: <u>Not applicable</u>
- Interpretation: <u>Junctional rhythm</u>
- Treatment: <u>If the patient is asymptomatic, watch the rhythm. If symptomatic, give atropine, dopamine, or epinephrine. Possible pacemaker.</u>
- Discussion
    - **Rate and rhythm:** The atrial rate and the ventricular rate are the same, but the rhythm is irregular for no obvious reason. There is no early (premature) beat, so the cause of the irregularity is unknown. This will sometimes happen in relation to the patient's breathing patterns. The changes in pressure inside the chest related to inspiration and expiration will sometimes cause changes in heart rhythm as the increase and decrease of chest pressures make it easier and harder for the heart to pump against the pressure.
    - **P wave origin:** If one looks at the lower rhythm, there is no P wave seen at all. That is probably due to lead placement and is a good example of how lead placement can alter an interpretation. With the QRS slightly widened, this could be mistaken for an accelerated idioventricular rhythm. However, the P waves can be seen in the upper rhythm, thereby ruling out an idioventricular rhythm.
    - **PR interval:** The PR interval is narrow, making this junctional in origin.

Answers to Chapter 3: Heart Blocks

EKG 3.1

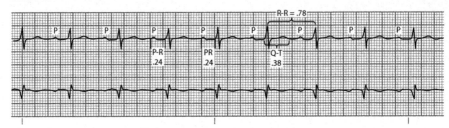

- Rate: Atrial <u>80 beats per minute (bpm)</u> Ventricular <u>80 bpm</u>
- Rhythm: Regular
- P wave origin: <u>SA node</u>
- PR interval: <u>0.24 seconds (consistent)</u>
- QRS: <u>0.10 seconds</u>
- QT interval: <u>0.38 seconds (R-R interval = 0.78 seconds)</u>
- Underlying rhythm: <u>Sinus rhythm</u>
- Variant: <u>Prolonged PR interval</u>
- Interpretation: <u>Sinus rhythm with first-degree atrioventricular (AV) block</u>
- Treatment: <u>There is usually no treatment for this rhythm; however, the patient should be assessed for possible contributing factors. If possible, medications may need to be adjusted (Bucher, 2014; Diehl, 2011).</u>
- Discussion

  - **Rate and rhythm:** The atrial and ventricular rates are the same with one-to-one conduction and the rhythm is regular. The rate is within normal limits.
  - **P wave origin:** All the P waves are consistent in configuration, indicating that they are originating from the sinoatrial (SA) node.
  - **PR interval:** The PR interval is consistently longer than normal, suggesting that an AV block is present even though all the sinus impulses are getting through to cause ventricular conduction.
  - **QRS and QT intervals:** The QRS complexes are all consistent and narrow, indicating normal conduction through the ventricles. The QT interval is less than one half the R-R interval.
  - **Conclusion:** Everything is normal except for the prolonged PR interval. That would make this a sinus rhythm with first-degree AV block.

EKG 3.2

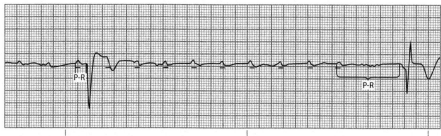

- Rate: Atrial 100 bpm Ventricular 20 bpm
- Rhythm: Not applicable
- P wave origin: SA node
- PR interval: Inconsistent
- QRS: #1 = 0.12 seconds, #2 = 0.20 seconds
- QT interval: Not applicable
- Underlying rhythm: Third degree (complete) heart block
- Variant: Atrioventricular block
- Interpretation: Complete heart block (third-degree heart block)
- Treatment: Pacemaker
- Discussion
  - **Rate:** The atrial rate is greater than the ventricular rate because there are more P waves than QRS complexes. That indicates some type of block.
  - **Rhythm:** The rhythm of the P waves is consistent until near the end. With only two beats available to use as a gauge, the rhythm of the ventricles is not able to be determined, but remember that the normal rate of the ventricles when they become the pacemaker of the heart is less than 40 bpm (beats per minute). Here it is 20 bpm.
  - **P wave origin:** The P waves are all consistent in configuration, indicating that they are all coming from the same place. It is assumed that the place of origin is the SA node.
  - **PR interval:** The PR intervals are inconsistent, indicating a complete (third degree) heart block. The atria and ventricles are working independent of each other.

EKG 3.3

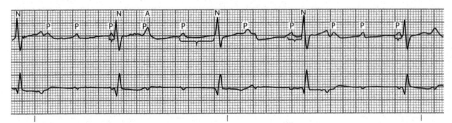

- Rate: Atrial <u>100 bpm</u> Ventricular <u>40 bpm</u>

- Rhythm: Regular

- P wave origin: <u>SA node</u>

- PR interval: <u>Variable</u>

- QRS: <u>0.12 seconds</u>

- QT interval: <u>Not applicable</u>

- Underlying rhythm: <u>Third-degree heart block</u>

- Variant: <u>More P waves than QRS complexes; inconsistent PR interval; atria and ventricles working independently</u>

- Interpretation: <u>Third-degree heart block</u>

- Treatment: <u>Third-degree heart block is different from the other heart blocks in that no impulses get through the AV node. For that reason, medications, such as atropine, are probably not effective. They may produce more P waves, but none are getting through the AV node so the ventricular rate will be little affected. If atropine is used, along with other catecholamines, such as dopamine or epinephrine, it is usually given to support blood pressure. The only true treatment for this dysrhythmia is a pacemaker. All other treatments are usually supportive until pacing can be initiated (Bucher, 2014).</u>

- Discussion

  - **Rate:** The atrial rate is greater than the ventricular rate because there are more P waves than QRS complexes. That indicates some type of block.
  - **Rhythm:** The rhythm of the P waves is consistent although some are distorted because they are bumping into T waves. The ventricular rhythm is fairly consistent, but remember that the normal rate of the ventricles when they become the pacemaker of the heart is less than 40 bpm. Here it is 40 bpm.
  - **P wave origin:** The P waves are all consistent in configuration, indicating that they are all coming from the same place. It is assumed that the place of origin is the SA node.
  - **PR interval:** The PR intervals are inconsistent, indicating a complete (third degree) heart block. The atria and ventricles are working independent of each other.

EKG 3.4

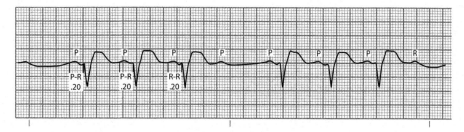

- Rate: Atrial <u>80 bpm</u> Ventricular <u>60 bpm</u>
- Rhythm: <u>Irregular</u>
- P wave origin: <u>SA node</u>
- PR interval: <u>0.20 seconds (consistent)</u>
- QRS: <u>0.16 seconds</u>
- QT interval: <u>0.38 seconds (R-R interval = 0.70 seconds)</u>
- Underlying rhythm: <u>Sinus rhythm</u>
- Variant: <u>Second-degree heart block (Mobitz II)</u>
- Interpretation: <u>Sinus rhythm with second-degree heart block (Mobitz II)</u>
- Treatment: <u>This is still a second-degree heart block, meaning that some impulses are getting through and others are not, but it is unpredictable and that is what makes it dangerous. Yet, because some of the P waves are getting through, atropine is still the drug of choice, in the hope that creating more P waves will allow more to get through. Otherwise, a temporary pacemaker may be needed while awaiting the insertion of a permanent pacemaker (Bucher, 2014, Diehl, 2011).</u>
- Discussion
    - **Rate:** There are more P waves than QRS complexes. That indicates some type of block.
    - **Rhythm:** The rhythm is irregular because there is a complex missing. There should be a QRS after P wave number 4, and there is not.
    - **P wave origin:** The P waves are consistent in configuration, indicating a common focal point of origin. That point is assumed to be the SA node.
    - **PR interval:** The PR intervals are consistent, indicating a second-degree (Mobitz II) heart block.

EKG 3.5

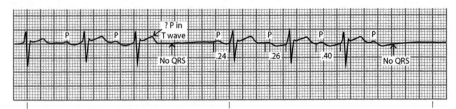

- Rate: Atrial <u>60 bpm</u> Ventricular <u>50 bpm</u>

- Rhythm: Irregular

- P wave origin: <u>SA node</u>

- PR interval: <u>Progressively longer (0.24, 0.36, 0.40 seconds)</u>

- QRS: <u>0.12 seconds</u>

- QT interval: <u>0.38 seconds (R-R interval = 0.84 seconds)</u>

- Underlying rhythm: <u>Sinus rhythm</u>

- Variant: <u>Second-degree heart block (Mobitz I)</u>

- Interpretation: <u>Sinus rhythm with second-degree heart block (Mobitz I)</u>

- Treatment: <u>The first step in treating any dysrhythmia is to check the patient. If the patient is tolerating the rhythm, and it is suspected that this rhythm may be temporary, then a "wait and watch" philosophy may be warranted (Diehl, 2014). The patient's medication list should be evaluated to detect any medications that may cause this rhythm, and those medications that are withheld. If, however, the patient is not tolerating this rhythm (if the patient is hypotensive, complaining of chest discomfort, etc.), then atropine is the drug of choice to help stimulate the SA node further. If some of the P waves are getting through and some are not, the hope is that creating more P waves will allow more to get through. If that does not work, a pacemaker may be necessary (Bucher, 2014; Diehl, 2011).</u>

- Discussion

  - **Rate:** There are more P waves than QRS complexes. This indicates some type of block. Notice how the T wave after beat number 3 looks slightly different from the other T waves. Most likely, there is a P wave in there causing the distortion.
  - **Rhythm:** The rhythm is irregular because there is a complex missing. There should be QRS complexes after P waves 4 and 7, and there are none.
  - **P wave origin:** The P waves are consistent in configuration, indicating a common focal point of origin. That point is assumed to be the SA node.
  - **PR interval:** The PR intervals get progressively longer, indicating a "weakening" of the AV node before there is a P wave without a QRS, indicating an inability of the AV node to pass the atrial impulse on to the ventricles. This is diagnostic of second-degree heart block Mobitz II.

Answers to Chapter 4: Ventricular Rhythms

EKG 4.1

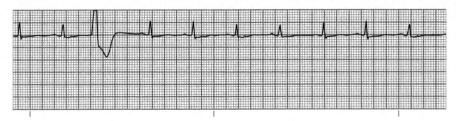

- Rate: Atrial <u>70 beats per minute (bpm)</u> Ventricular <u>80 bpm</u>
- Rhythm: Irregular due to early beat
- P wave origin: <u>SA node</u>
- PR interval: <u>0.18 seconds (consistent)</u>
- QRS: <u>0.08 seconds (early beat = 0.16 seconds)</u>
- QT interval: <u>0.24 seconds (QT = 0.70 seconds)</u>
- Underlying rhythm: <u>Sinus rhythm</u>
- Variant: <u>Early ventricular beat (no P wave and wide QRS)</u>
- Interpretation: <u>Sinus rhythm with premature ventricular contraction (PVC)</u>
- Treatment: <u>If PVCs are occasional and not close to the T waves of the patient's normal beats, the patient probably will not need treatment. However, if they are more than "occasional" or close to the T waves, the cause of the PVCs needs to be investigated. Perhaps the most common cause is hypoxia, so, if possible, the first order of treatment would be to administer oxygen Bucher, 20104; Diehl, 2011). Electrolyte levels, especially potassium and magnesium, need to be examined and treated if necessary (Bucher, 2014; Diehl, 2011: Sinz, 2011). Medications, such as amiodarone, procainamide, lidocaine, and/or beta-adrenergic blockers, can be used for control of PVCs. However, hypoxemia is a major cause of PVCs (Sinz, 2011), and is perhaps the easiest cause to treat. If the patient is having PVCs, the first thing to do is provide oxygen.</u>
- Discussion
    - **Rate:** There are more QRS complexes than P waves. That would suggest the presence of a beat coming from either the junction or the ventricle.
    - **Rhythm:** The rhythm is irregular due to beat number 3 being early.
    - **P wave origin:** The P waves are all consistent in configuration, suggesting that the point of origin is the SA node, but beat number 3 does not have a P wave.
    - **PR interval:** The PR intervals are consistent and within normal limits.
    - **QRS:** All the QRS complexes are within normal limits except for beat number 3, which is wide and has the T wave going in the opposite direction of the QRS complexes main deflection (the R wave).
    - **Conclusion:** The underlying rhythm is sinus in origin as indicated by its normal rate and overall regular rhythm. Beat number 3, however, has no P wave and is wide in configuration, indicating that this beat is arising from the ventricles and is premature. Therefore, this is a sinus rhythm with a PVC.

EKG 4.2

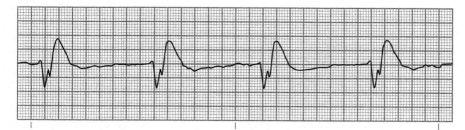

- Rate: Atrial 0 Ventricular 40 bpm
- Rhythm: Regular
- P wave origin: Not applicable
- PR interval: Not applicable
- QRS: 0.28 seconds
- QT interval: Not applicable
- Underlying rhythm: Idioventricular rhythm
- Variant: Idioventricular rhythm
- Interpretation: Idioventricular rhythm
- Treatment: This is not a rhythm that you want to get rid of. Antiarrhythmics, such as amiodarone, lidocaine, and so worth, will wipe out this rhythm and what will be left is nothing. This is a rhythm that you want to replace with something else. Ideally, it would be nice to replace this with a rhythm coming from the SA node. The medication of choice to do that would be atropine (Diehl, 2011; Sinz, 2011). Epinephrine or dopamine may also be used if atropine is not effective (Sinz, 2011). When the rhythm is refractory to medication therapy, transcutaneous pacing may be advisable until a transvenous pacemaker can be placed (Diehl, 20011; Sinz, 2011). Basic cardiac life support (BCLS) and advanced cardiac life support (ACLS) may be required if the patient is not tolerating this rhythm (Sinz, 2011).
- Discussion
    - **Rate and rhythm:** There are no P waves and no atrial rhythm. The ventricular rate is 40 bpm, which is an expected rate if the ventricles are the main focus of origin. Remember that the normal rate for the ventricles is 40 bpm or less (not conducive to longevity). Also remember that the reason this rhythm is present is because there is no functioning focus in the SA node, atria, or atrioventricular (AV) node. The rhythm is regular.
    - **QRS:** The QRS is wide, suggesting that these impulses are arising in the ventricles.

EKG 4.3

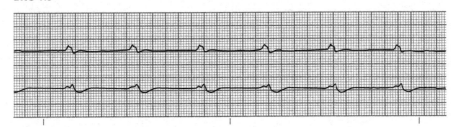

- Rate: Atrial <u>0</u> Ventricular <u>60 bpm</u>
- Rhythm: Regular
- P wave origin: <u>Not applicable</u>
- PR interval: <u>Not applicable</u>
- QRS: <u>0.16 seconds</u>
- QT interval: <u>Not applicable</u>
- Underlying rhythm: <u>Idioventricular rhythm</u>
- Variant: <u>Increased rate</u>
- Interpretation: <u>Accelerated idioventricular rhythm</u>
- Treatment: <u>Sometimes the healthcare provider will adopt a "wait and see" tactic with this rhythm. As long as the rate remains stable and the patient is tolerating it, there is a chance that the issue causing this rhythm may resolve itself and the SA node may reassert itself. However, even if the provider opts for the "wait and see" method, atropine, epinephrine, dopamine, and a transcutaneous pacemaker should be readily available in case the rhythm decays into its slower form (Diehl, 2011).</u>
- Discussion
    - **Rate and rhythm:** There are no P waves, and the ventricular rate is 60 bpm, which is faster than the expected rate if the focus of origination is the ventricle (normal is less than 40 bpm). The rhythm is regular.
    - **QRS:** The QRS complexes are wide and have no P wave before them, suggesting that they are ventricular in origin.
    - **Conclusion:** Since this is a ventricular rhythm that is present because there is no functional source above the ventricle (SA or junctional), it is considered idioventricular, and, because it is going faster than it should, but not so fast as to the of lethal ventricular tachycardia (VT), this rhythm is called an *accelerated idioventricular rhythm.*

EKG 4.4

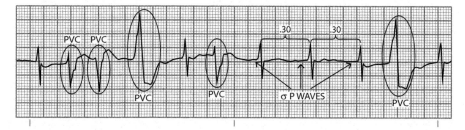

PVC, premature ventricular contraction.

- Rate: Atrial Unable to count Ventricular 100 bpm
- Rhythm: Irregular due to premature beats
- P wave origin: Unable to determine
- PR interval: Not applicable
- QRS: Variable widths
- QT interval: Not applicable
- Underlying rhythm: Atrial versus junctional
- Variant: Premature ventricular contractions
- Interpretation: Supraventricular tachycardia with multifocal PVCs
- Treatment: There is a little more urgency in treating multifocal PVCs than in treating unifocal PVCs. However, the criteria and treatment are otherwise similar. If the PVCs are infrequent, there may be no treatment. Otherwise, the first order of treatment would be to administer oxygen.
  Electrolyte levels, especially potassium and magnesium, need to be examined and treated if necessary (Bucher, 2014; Diehl, 2011). Medications, such as amiodarone, procainamide, lidocaine, and/or beta-adrenergic blockers, can be used for control of PVCs (Bucher, 2014; Diehl, 2011).
- Discussion
  - **Rate and rhythm:** I cannot see P waves, but the QRS complexes (except for beats 2, 3, 4, and 10) are narrow and look fairly normal, indicating a supraventricular focus. The ventricular rate is 100 bpm. I can see beats 7, 8, and 9 quite clearly and believe that these are indicative of the patient's underlying rhythm. That rhythm seems regular, ruling out atrial fibrillation (A-fib) as an underlying rhythm. However, the overall rhythm is irregular due to early beats 2, 3, 4, 6, and 10.
  - **P-wave origin and PR interval:** Because the P waves are not seen, the underlying rhythm could be junctional in origin. However, there is a chance that the P waves are small and difficult to see, and that would make this, at least, atrial in origin. I would need a longer strip of just the underlying rhythm to be sure, so I will compromise and call this *supraventricular* (that really means "I don't know, but it's not coming from the ventricles"). Since there is no clearly defined P wave, there is no PR interval.

■ **QRS complexes:** The QRS complexes that make up the underlying rhythm (beats 1, 5, 7, 8, and 9) look the same and are narrow, indicating that they are coming from the same place and traveling through the same tissue. Most likely, that tissue is the normal conductive pathway of the ventricles. The remaining QRS complexes all are wide and look different from one another. Actually beats 2 and 6 look similar and beats 3 and 10 look similar, but 2 and 6 do not look like 3 and 10. This indicates that there are at least two ectopic foci in the ventricles. Add to that the fact that beat number 3 does not look like any of the other beats. That makes three ectopic foci. This is an irritable ventricle, and the risk of lethal arrhythmia is very high.

EKG 4.5

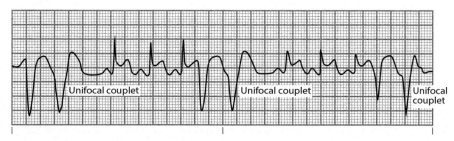

Source: Landrum, M. A. (2013). *Fast facts about EKGs for nurses: The rules of identifying EKGs in a nutshell* (p. 69). New York, NY: Springer Publishing.

- Rate: Atrial <u>60 bpm</u> Ventricular <u>120 bpm</u>

- Rhythm: <u>Irregular due to PVCs</u>

- P wave origin: <u>SA node</u>

- PR interval: <u>0.18 seconds</u>

- QRS: <u>0.10 seconds/0.28 seconds</u>

- QT interval: <u>0.24 (R-R interval = 0.44 seconds)</u>

- Underlying rhythm: <u>Sinus</u>

- Variant: <u>Premature ventricular contraction couplet</u>

- Interpretation: <u>Sinus rhythm with PVC couplets</u>

- Treatment: <u>If PVCs are occasional and not close to the T waves of the patient's normal beats, they probably will not need treatment. However, if they are more than "occasional" or close to the T waves, the cause of the PVCs needs to be investigated. Perhaps the most common cause is hypoxia, so, if possible, the first order of treatment would be to administer oxygen (Bucher, 2014; Diehl, 2011). Electrolyte levels, especially potassium and magnesium, need to be examined and treated if necessary (Bucher, 2014; Diehl, 2011; Sinz, 2011). Medications, such as amiodarone, procainamide, lidocaine, and/or beta-adrenergic blockers, can be used for control of PVCs.</u>

- Discussion

    - **Rate and rhythm:** The atrial rate is 60 bpm since there are six P waves, and the ventricular rate is 120 bpm since there are 12 QRS complexes in the 6-second strip. The rhythm, however, is irregular since beats 6 and 7 come early as do beats 11 and 12, and so are premature somethings. We cannot see what precedes beats 1 and 2 so it cannot be said that they are premature, but since they look like the other premature beats, it's probably a safe bet.

    - **P wave origin and PR interval:** The P waves, when present, look to be the same, indicating that they are coming from the same focus—assumedly the SA node. The PR interval is within normal limits.

    - **QRS and QT interval:** The QRS complexes of the sinus beats are narrow and look the same. Beats 6 and 7 and beats 11 and 12, however, are wide and bizarre looking since the T wave is going in the opposite direction of the main defection (S wave). These are ventricular in origin, and the two together make them PVCs in a couplet configuration. The QT interval is more than one half the R-R interval. This may bear watching.

EKG 4.6

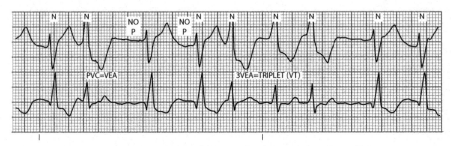

PVC, premature ventricular contraction; VEA, ventricular ectopic activity; VT, ventricular tachycardia.

- Rate: Atrial <u>0</u> Ventricular <u>90 bpm</u>

- Rhythm: <u>Irregular</u>

- P wave origin: <u>Not applicable</u>

- PR interval: <u>Not applicable</u>

- QRS: <u>0.18/0.20 seconds</u>

- QT interval: <u>Not applicable</u>

- Underlying rhythm: <u>A-fib</u>

- Variant: <u>Ventricular ectopic activity (VEA) with a triplet</u>

- Interpretation: <u>A-fib with VEA and a triplet (short rub of ventricular tachycardia [VT])</u>

- Treatment: <u>The first order of treatment would be to administer oxygen. Electrolyte levels, especially potassium and magnesium, need to be examined and treated if necessary (Bucher, 2014; Diehl, 2011). Medications, such as amiodarone, procainamide, lidocaine, and/or beta-adrenergic blockers, can be used for control (Bucher, 2014; Diehl, 2011). Also, note the three ventricular complexes that are together. This is a triplet. In some circles, a triplet is considered a short run of VT.</u>

- Discussion

  - **Rate:** In the preceding rhythm, there are no P waves anywhere. This, then, is A-fib with VEA. The treatment should be the same as with PVCs, but these are not technically PVCs.
  - **Rhythm:** The R-R interval between any two complexes that look alike is inconsistent, suggesting that if the ventricular activity were not there, the rhythm would be irregular anyway. The ventricular beats merely add to the irregularity.
  - **P wave origin and PR interval:** There are no P waves. There is no PR interval.
  - **QRS:** Complexes 1, 3, 4, 8, and 9 fall within the upper limits of normal, but complexes 2, 5, 6, and 7 are wide and ventricular in origin.
  - **Of note:** The underlying rhythm has no P waves and is irregular, making this, by definition, an atrial fibrillation. However, there are ventricular beats present. The lack of a regular rhythm makes it impossible to state that the ventricular beats are early or late, so they cannot be called *PVCs*. They are called *ventricular ectopic activity* or *VEA*. However, three in a row is still a triplet or a "short run of V-tach" (ventricular tachycardia).

EKG 4.7

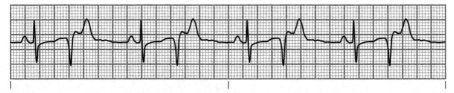

Source: Landrum, M. A. (2013). *Fast facts about EKGs for nurses: The rules of identifying EKGs in a nutshell* (p.101). New York, NY: Springer Publishing.

- Rate: Atrial 40 bpm Ventricular 80 bpm
- Rhythm: Irregular due to early beats
- P wave origin: SA node
- PR interval: 0.20 seconds
- QRS: 0.08/0.18 seconds
- QT interval: Not applicable
- Underlying rhythm: Sinus rhythm
- Variant: Bigeminal PVCs
- Interpretation: Sinus rhythm with bigeminal PVCs
- Treatment: The first order of treatment is to administer oxygen. Electrolyte levels, especially potassium and magnesium, need to be examined and treated if necessary (Bucher, 2014; Diehl, 2011). Medications, such as amiodarone, procainamide, lidocaine, and/or beta-adrenergic blockers, can be used for control of PVCs (Bucher, 2014; Diehl, 2011).
- Discussion
    - **Rate:** There are four P waves between the first and third 3-second markers giving an atrial rate of 40 bpm. There are eight QRS complexes, three of which are ventricular in origin (no P wave and wide), and all of those are identical.
    - **Rhythm:** The rhythm is irregular due to the early ventricular beats.
    - **P wave origin:** The P waves that are present all look the same and are probably sinus in origin.
    - **PR interval:** Falls within the normal range.
    - **QRS:** The QRS complexes that are preceded by P waves fall within the normal standard. The premature QRS complexes are wide and have the T wave going in a direction opposite of the main deflection. They all look the same, making them unifocal PVCs.
    - **Interpretation:** The underlying rhythm is a sinus rhythm, but premature ventricular contractions are present and originate from the same place in a bigeminal (every other beat) pattern.

EKG 4.8

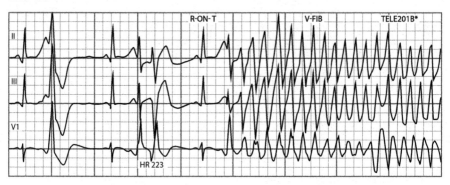

Source: Knechtel, M. (2017). *EKGs for the nurse practitioner and physician assistant* (2nd ed., p. 172). New York, NY: Springer Publishing.

- Rate: Atrial 10 bpm Ventricular Greater than 200 bpm

- Rhythm: Irregular

- P wave origin: SA node

- PR interval: Not applicable

- QRS: Wide

- QT interval: Not applicable

- Underlying rhythm: Sinus rhythm

- Variant: R-on-T phenomenon, ventricular tachycardia deteriorating to fibrillation

- Interpretation: Ventricular fibrillation caused by R-on-T phenomenon

- Treatment: Assess the patient. If the patient is awake or breathing, he or she is not in ventricular fibrillation. Check the patient's leads. If the patient is unresponsive, begin cardiopulmonary resuscitation (CPR) and call for help. Institute ACLS protocols as soon as possible.

   It's important to understand that the heart is not pumping blood, but that does not mean the heart is not working. It is working very hard, but it is not working in a coordinated fashion. Something has happened to cause all the cells in the heart to depolarize and repolarize randomly. The end result is a lot of work being done, but the lack of coordination and cooperation leads to no effective end result or heart contraction.

   Without blood flow, no more resources (oxygen and glucose) are being brought in. In the meantime, waste is being produced and there is no blood flow to carry the waste away from the heart tissue.

   In approximately 90 seconds (1½ minutes), the heart will be so toxic, that it will not be able to respond to electrical shock. However, there is a solution. Oxygen must be replaced, and toxic waste must be removed. Blood flow and oxygen supply must be restored. The key to that is CPR.

CPR will not convert ventricular fibrillation back into a sinus rhythm. Only defibrillation will do that. The only way out of "V-fib" is to "D-fib." However, CPR will provide circulation and oxygenation enough to buy time so that defibrillation will be successful.

When a ventricular fibrillation first begins, the rhythm is "coarse" looking. As time goes on, the rhythm will become finer and finer until it becomes a straight line. The progressive deterioration of the rhythm (as the rhythm becomes "finer") indicates the increasing level of toxicity in the heart muscle. This is of great concern as the more toxic the muscle is, the less likely it is to respond to defibrillation. Fortunately, there is a medication that has the unique ability to convert fine fibrillation back into coarse fibrillation.

Epinephrine (Adrenalin) is that medication. Epinephrine is a catecholamine that is also a potent vasoconstrictor that has a very short duration (Comerford, 2016). It is possible that the sudden constriction of the coronary arteries may force "toxic" blood out of the heart and then the relaxation of the arteries soon afterward may "suck" oxygenated blood in. In that way, it can convert the fine fibrillation back to coarse fibrillation. For that reason, this medication is given every 3 to 5 minutes during a cardiac arrest (code) situation.

Again, epinephrine will not break the rhythm. It will only make it more susceptible to defibrillation. However, the cause of the fibrillation is still not known and may never be known, so antiarrhythmics are used to prevent the heart from going back into fibrillation once defibrillation successfully terminates it. Amiodarone and lidocaine are two of those antiarrhythmic medications. Use per ACLS protocols.

- Discussion

  - **Rate:** The first beat has a P wave giving an atrial rate of 10 bpm. The remaining beats are ventricular in origin and have no P wave so this adds to the ventricular rate. Everything after beat 1 is arrhythmic and cannot be added to the rate.
  - **Rhythm:** This rhythm starts out with a sinus beat, but a premature beat strikes the T wave of that beat, leading to a very coarse V-fib. Technically, the complexes are well defined, making it more of a V-tach, but it will deteriorate to V-fib quickly.
  - **P wave origin:** The first beat is normal in configuration, indicating a sinus node origin.
  - **PR interval:** The PR interval for the first beats is not measurable due to the quality of the strip, but, in reality, it is inconsequential because the patient has gone into V-fib and will die if the V-fib is not corrected quickly.
  - **QRS:** The QRS complexes are all wide and have no P waves after the first complex. This indicates a ventricular origin. However, the complexes are getting smaller, indicating that the rhythm is deteriorating rapidly.
  - **Interpretation:** The major focus here should be on the R-on-T phenomenon leading to the ventricular fibrillation.

EKG 4.9

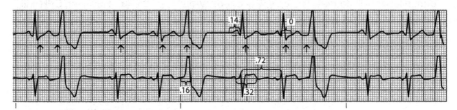

- Rate: Atrial <u>50 bpm</u> Ventricular <u>80 bpm</u>

- Rhythm: Irregular due to premature beats

- P wave origin: <u>SA node; premature beats have no P waves</u>

- PR interval: <u>0.14 seconds</u>

- QRS: <u>0.10 seconds; premature QRS complexes are 0.16 seconds wide</u>

- QT interval: <u>0.32 seconds (R-R interval = 0.72 seconds)</u>

- Underlying rhythm: <u>Sinus rhythm</u>

- Variant: <u>Premature ventricular contractions (every third beat)</u>

- Interpretation: <u>Sinus rhythm with trigeminal PVCs</u>

- Treatment: <u>The first order of treatment would be to administer oxygen. Electrolyte levels, especially potassium and magnesium, need to be examined and treated if necessary (Bucher, 2011; Diehl, 2011). Medications, such as amiodarone, procainamide, lidocaine, and/or beta-adrenergic blockers, can be used to control PVCs.</u>

- Discussion

  - **Rate:** There are five P waves between the first and third 3-second markers, giving an atrial rate of 50 bpm. There are eight QRS complexes between the first and third 3 second markers. Beats 2, 5, and 8 are ventricular in origin (no P wave and wide), and all three are identical.
  - **Rhythm:** The rhythm is irregular due to the early ventricular beats.
  - **P wave origin:** The P waves that are present all look the same and are probably sinus in origin.
  - **PR interval:** Falls within the normal range.
  - **QRS:** The QRS complexes that are preceded by P waves fall within the normal standard. The premature QRS complexes are wide and have the T wave going in the opposite direction of the main deflection. All three look the same, making them unifocal PVCs.
  - **Interpretation:** The underlying rhythm is a sinus rhythm, but premature ventricular contractions are present and originate from the same place in a trigeminal pattern.

EKG 4.10

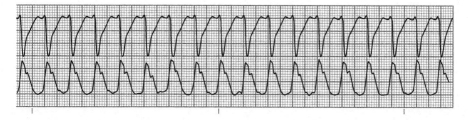

- Rate: Atrial 0 Ventricular 150 bpm
- Rhythm: Regular
- P wave origin: Not applicable
- PR interval: Not applicable
- QRS: 0.14 seconds
- QT interval: Not applicable
- Underlying rhythm: Ventricular
- Variant: Tachycardia
- Interpretation: Ventricular tachycardia
- Treatment: Determine responsiveness of the patient. If the patient is conscious, apply oxygen and treat with intravenous amiodarone or lidocaine following ACLS protocols. If the patient is conscious but unstable (i.e., has a low blood pressure and symptoms of decompensation), synchronized cardioversion may be needed to terminate the rhythm (Diehl, 2011; Marcum, 2013).
- Discussion: If the patient is unconscious, the dysrhythmia must be treated as if it is ventricular fibrillation. The patient is effectively in cardiac arrest. The ACLS protocol must be instituted immediately. CPR must be initiated, and the patient defibrillated as soon as possible. If there is no change in the rhythm, CPR should be continued. Epinephrine should be given followed by CPR for 2 minutes and then defibrillation should be attempted again. With no change in rhythm, CPR is resumed and amiodarone given intravenously and circulated (using CPR) for 2 minutes, followed by another defibrillation attempt. If there is no change, CPR is to be continued and epinephrine repeated. This is followed by CPR for 2 minutes and another defibrillation attempt. If there is still no change, IV (intravenous) lidocaine is given per protocol, circulated for 2 minutes, and defibrillation is attempted again (Sinz, 2011).

EKG 4.11

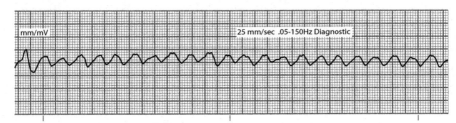

mm/mV   25 mm/sec .05-150Hz Diagnostic

- Rate: Atrial <u>0</u> Ventricular <u>0</u>

- Rhythm: Not applicable

- P wave origin: <u>Not applicable</u>

- QRS: <u>Not applicable</u>

- QT interval: <u>Not applicable</u>

- Underlying rhythm: <u>Ventricular fibrillation (coarse)</u>

- Variant: <u>Ventricular fibrillation (coarse)</u>

- Interpretation: <u>Ventricular fibrillation (coarse)</u>

- Treatment: <u>Assess the patient. If the patient is awake or breathing, he or she is not in ventricular fibrillation. Check the patient's leads. If the patient is unresponsive, begin CPR and call for help. Institute ACLS protocols as soon as possible.</u>

- Discussion: It's important to understand that the heart is not pumping blood, but that does not mean the heart is not working. It is working very hard, but it is not working in a coordinated fashion. Something has happened to cause all of the cells in the heart to depolarize and repolarize randomly. The end result is a lot of work being done, but the lack of coordination and cooperation leads to no effective end result or heart contraction.

  Without blood flow, no more resources (oxygen and glucose) are being brought in. In the meantime, waste is being produced and there is no blood flow to carry the waste away from the heart tissue.

  In approximately 90 seconds (1½ minutes), the heart will be so toxic, that it will not be able to respond to electrical shock. However, there is a solution. Oxygen must be replaced and toxic waste must be removed. Blood flow and oxygen supply must be restored. The key to that is CPR.

  CPR will not convert ventricular fibrillation back into a sinus rhythm. Only defibrillation will do that. However, CPR will provide circulation and oxygenation enough to buy you time so that defibrillation will be successful.

  When ventricular fibrillation first begins, the rhythm is "coarse" looking. As time goes on, the rhythm will become finer and finer until it becomes a straight line. The progressive deterioration of the rhythm (as the rhythm becomes "finer") indicates the increasing level of toxicity in the heart muscle. This is of great concern because the more toxic the muscle is, the less likely it is that it will respond to defibrillation. Fortunately, there is a medication that has the unique ability to convert fine fibrillation back into coarse fibrillation.

Epinephrine (Adrenalin) is that medication. Epinephrine is a catecholamine that is also a potent vasoconstrictor that has a very short duration (Comerford, 2016). It is possible that the sudden constriction of the coronary arteries may force "toxic" blood out of the heart and then the relaxation of the arteries soon afterward may "suck" oxygenated blood in. In that way, it can convert the fine fibrillation back to the coarse fibrillation. For that reason, this medication is given every 3 to 5 minutes during a cardiac arrest (code) situation.

Again, epinephrine will not break the rhythm. It will only make it more susceptible to defibrillation. However, the cause of the fibrillation is still not known and may never be known, so antiarrhythmics are used to prevent the heart from going back into fibrillation once defibrillation successfully terminates the fibrillation. Amiodarone and lidocaine are two of those antiarrhythmic medications. Use per ACLS protocols.

EKG 4.12

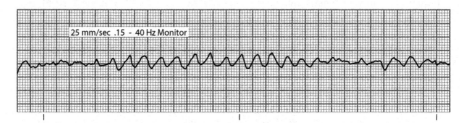

25 mm/sec .15 - 40 Hz Monitor

Source: Knechtel, M. (2017). *EKGs for the nurse practitioner and physician assistant* (p. 176). New York, NY: Springer Publishing.

- Rate: Atrial <u>0</u> Ventricular <u>0</u>

- Rhythm: Not applicable

- P wave origin: <u>Not applicable</u>

- PR interval: <u>Not applicable</u>

- QRS: <u>Not applicable</u>

- QT interval: <u>Not applicable</u>

- Underlying rhythm: <u>Ventricular fibrillation</u>

- Variant: <u>Fine</u>

- Interpretation: <u>Fine ventricular fibrillation</u>

- Treatment: <u>Assess the patient. If the patient is awake or breathing, he or she is not in ventricular fibrillation. Check the patient's leads. If the patient is unresponsive, begin CPR and call for help. Institute ACLS protocols as soon as possible.</u>

- Discussion: It's important to understand that the heart is not pumping blood, but that does not mean that the heart is not working. It is working very hard, but it is not working in a coordinated fashion. Something has happened to cause all the cells in the heart to depolarize and repolarize randomly. The end result is a lot of work being done, but the lack of coordination and cooperation leads to no effective end result or heart contraction.

    Without blood flow, no more resources (oxygen and glucose) are being brought in. In the meantime, waste is being produced and there is no blood flow to carry the waste away from the heart tissue.

    In approximately 90 seconds (1½ minutes), the heart will be so toxic that it will not be able to respond to electrical shock. However, there is a solution. Oxygen must be replaced, and toxic waste must be removed. Blood flow and oxygen supply must be restored. The key to that is CPR.

    CPR will not convert ventricular fibrillation back into a sinus rhythm. Only defibrillation will do that. The only way out of "V-fib" is to "D-fib." However, CPR will provide circulation and oxygenation enough to buy you time so that defibrillation will be successful.

    When ventricular fibrillation first starts, the rhythm is "coarse" looking. As time goes on, the rhythm will become finer and finer until it becomes a straight line. The progressive deterioration of the rhythm (as the rhythm becomes "finer") indicates the increasing level of toxicity in the heart muscle. This is of great concern because the more toxic the muscle is, the less likely it will respond to defibrillation. Fortunately, there is a medication that has the unique ability to convert fine fibrillation back into coarse fibrillation.

Epinephrine (Adrenalin) is that medication. Epinephrine is a catecholamine that is also a potent vasoconstrictor that has a very short duration (Comerford, 2016). It is possible that the sudden constriction of the coronary arteries may force "toxic" blood out of the heart and then the relaxation of the arteries soon afterward may "suck" oxygenated blood in. In that way, it can convert the fine fibrillation back into coarse fibrillation. For that reason, this medication is given every 3 to 5 minutes during a cardiac arrest (code) situation.

Again, epinephrine will not break the rhythm. It will only make it more susceptible to defibrillation. However, the cause of the fibrillation is still not known and may never be known, so antiarrhythmics are used to prevent the heart from going back into fibrillation once defibrillation successfully terminates it. Amiodarone and lidocaine are two of those antiarrhythmic medications. Use per ACLS protocols.

EKG 4.13

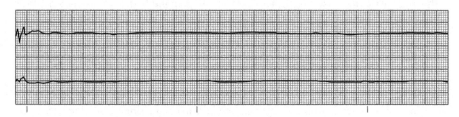

- Rate: Atrial <u>0</u> Ventricular <u>0</u>

- Rhythm: Not applicable

- P wave origin: <u>Not applicable</u>

- PR interval: <u>Not applicable</u>

- QRS: <u>Not applicable</u>

- QT interval: <u>Not applicable</u>

- Underlying rhythm: <u>Asystole</u>

- Variant: <u>Asystole</u>

- Interpretation: <u>Asystole</u>

- Treatment: <u>The fact is if someone is truly asystolic, there is no hope. Nothing is going to bring this person back. He or she is dead. If that is your attitude, then why try? If you have resigned yourself to this thought process, you have condemned your patient to death. There is, however, another way to look at this.</u>

- Discussion: What if this is not asystole? What if, instead, this is a very fine ventricular fibrillation? We can treat ventricular fibrillation. The solution is found in the preceding sections. If we think of asystole as a fine ventricular fibrillation, then our goal will be to convert the fine fibrillation to a coarse fibrillation so that we can defibrillate with a better chance of success. The drug of choice to do this is epinephrine (Adrenalin). Epinephrine, however, will not work unless we get circulation going, so CPR will be required followed by ACLS protocols.

EKG 4.14

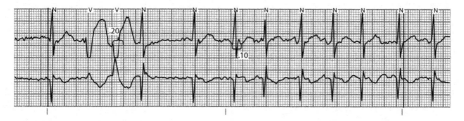

- Rate: Atrial <u>0</u> Ventricular <u>110 bpm</u>
- Rhythm: <u>Irregular</u>
- P wave origin: <u>Not applicable</u>
- PR interval: <u>Not applicable</u>
- QRS: <u>0.10 seconds (0.20 seconds for ventricular ectopic activity)</u>
- QT interval: <u>Not applicable</u>
- Underlying rhythm: <u>Atrial fibrillation</u>
- Variant: <u>Ventricular ectopic activity (couplet)</u>
- Interpretation: <u>Atrial fibrillation with VEA (couplet)</u>
- Treatment: <u>The first order of treatment would be to administer oxygen. Electrolyte</u>
  <u>levels, especially potassium and magnesium, need to be examined and treated</u>
  <u>if necessary (Bucher, 2014, Diehl, 2011). Medications, such as amiodarone,</u>
  <u>procainamide, lidocaine, and/or beta-adrenergic blockers, can be used for control</u>
  <u>(Bucher, 2014, Diehl, 2011). Also note the two ventricular complexes that are</u>
  <u>together. This is a couplet.</u>
- Discussion
  - **Rate:** With this rhythm, there are no P waves anywhere. This, then, is A-fib with VEA. The treatment should be the same as with PVCs, but they are not technically PVCs.
  - **Rhythm:** The R-R interval between any two complexes that look alike is inconsistent, suggesting that if the ventricular activity were not there, the rhythm would be irregular anyway. The ventricular beats merely add to the irregularity.
  - **P wave origin:** There are no P waves.
  - **PR interval:** There is no PR interval.
  - **QRS:** Complexes 2 and 3 are wide and ventricular in origin. The rest fall within the upper limits of normal.
  - The underlying rhythm has no P waves and is irregular, making this, by definition, an atrial fibrillation. However, ventricular beats are present. The lack of a regular rhythm makes it impossible to state that the ventricular beats are early or late so they cannot be called *PVCs*. They are called *VEA*. However, two in a row is still a couplet.

EKG 4.15

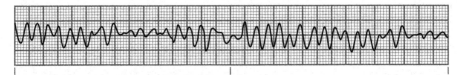

Source: Landrum, M. A. (2014). *Fast facts about EKGs for nurses The rules of identifying EKGs in a nutshell* (p. 74). New York, NY: Springer Publishing.

- Rate: Atrial <u>0</u> Ventricular <u>0</u>

- Rhythm: Not applicable

- P wave origin: <u>Not applicable</u>

- PR interval: <u>Not applicable</u>

- QRS: <u>Not applicable</u>

- QT interval: <u>Not applicable</u>

- Underlying rhythm: <u>Ventricular fibrillation</u>

- Variant: <u>Fine</u>

- Interpretation: <u>Fine ventricular fibrillation</u>

- Treatment: <u>Assess the patient. If the patient is awake or breathing, he or she is not in ventricular fibrillation. Check the patient's leads. If the patient is unresponsive, begin CPR and call for help. Institute ACLS protocols as soon as possible.</u>

- Discussion: It's important to understand that the heart is not pumping blood, but that does not mean that the heart is not working. It is working very hard, but it is not working in a coordinated fashion. Something has happened to cause all of the cells in the heart to depolarize and repolarize randomly. The end result is a lot of work being done, but the lack of coordination and cooperation leads to no effective end result or heart contraction.

    The fact that "work" is being done leads to resources being used up. Without blood flow, no more resources (oxygen and glucose) are being brought in. In the meantime, waste is being produced and there is no blood flow to carry the waste away from the heart tissue.

    In approximately 90 seconds (1½ minutes), the heart will be so toxic that it will not be able to respond to electrical shock. However, there is a solution. Oxygen must be replaced, and toxic waste must be removed. Blood flow and oxygen supply must be restored. The key to that is CPR.

    CPR will not convert ventricular fibrillation back into a sinus rhythm. Only defibrillation will do that. The only way out of "V-fib" is to "D-fib." However, CPR will provide circulation and oxygenation enough to buy you time so that defibrillation will be successful.

    When ventricular fibrillation first starts, the rhythm is "coarse" looking. As time goes on, the rhythm will become finer and finer until it becomes a straight line. The progressive deterioration of the rhythm (as the rhythm becomes "finer") indicates the increasing level of toxicity in the heart muscle. This is of great concern because the more toxic the muscle is, the less likely it is that it will respond to defibrillation.

Fortunately, there is a medication that has the unique ability to convert fine fibrillation back into coarse fibrillation.

Epinephrine (Adrenalin) is that medication. Epinephrine is a catecholamine that is also a potent vasoconstrictor that has a very short duration (Comerford, 2016). It is possible that the sudden constriction of the coronary arteries may force "toxic" blood out of the heart and then the relaxation of the arteries soon afterward may "suck" oxygenated blood in. In that way, it can convert the fine fibrillation back to coarse fibrillation. For that reason, this medication is given every 3 to 5 minutes during a cardiac arrest (code) situation. Again, epinephrine will not break the rhythm. It will only make it more susceptible to defibrillation. However, the cause of the fibrillation is still not known and may never be known, so antiarrhythmics are used to prevent the heart from going back into fibrillation once defibrillation successfully terminates the fibrillation. Amiodarone and lidocaine are two of those antiarrhythmic medications. Use per ACLS protocols.

EKG 4.16

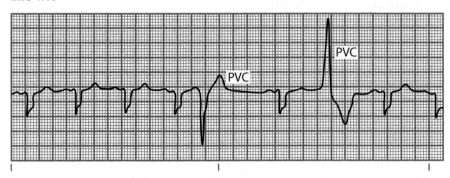

PVC, premature ventricular contraction.

Source: Landrum, M. A. (2014). *Fast facts about EKGs for nurses: The rules of identifying EKGs in a nutshell* (p. 69). New York, NY: Springer Publishing.

- Rate: Atrial <u>60 bpm</u> Ventricular <u>80 bpm</u>

- Rhythm: Irregular

- P wave origin: <u>Not applicable</u>

- PR interval: <u>Not applicable</u>

- QRS: <u>0.16 seconds</u>

- QT interval: <u>Not applicable</u>

- Underlying rhythm: <u>Sinus rhythm</u>

- Variant: <u>Multifocal premature ventricular contractions</u>

- Interpretation: <u>Sinus rhythm multifocal PVCs</u>

- Treatment: <u>We know that because the PVCs do not look the same, they are coming from different places. This means there is more than one irritable focus in the ventricle. This is more serious than having only one irritable focus. There is a greater chance of developing ventricular tachycardia or ventricular fibrillation. There is a little more urgency in treating multifocal PVCs than in treating unifocal PVCs. However, the criteria and treatment are otherwise similar. If the PVCs are infrequent, there may be no treatment needed. Otherwise, the first order of treatment would be to administer oxygen. Electrolyte levels, especially potassium and magnesium, need to be examined and treated if necessary (Bucher, 2014; Diehl, 2011). Medications, such as amiodarone, procainamide, lidocaine, and/or beta-adrenergic blockers, can be used for control of PVCs (Bucher, 2014; Diehl, 2011).</u>

- Discussion

  - **Rate and Rhythm:** There are more ventricular complexes and P waves. Beats 5 and 7 develop earlier than expected making this rhythm irregular.
  - **P wave origin:** The P waves that are present look the same and the PR intervals are with normal limits indicating the origin to be the SA node. Beats 5 and 7 have no P waves.

■ **QRS:** All of the QRS complexes appear normal with the exception of beats 5 and 7. They are wide and have the T wave going in the opposite direction from the main deflection of the complex indicating that these are ventricular in origin. Because they look different from one another, the indication is that they are coming from two different places in the ventricle making them multifocal.

EKG 4.17

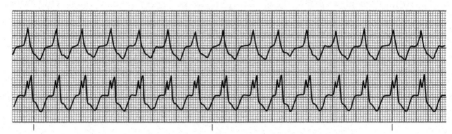

- Rate: Atrial <u>0</u> Ventricular <u>130 bpm</u>

- Rhythm: Regular

- P wave origin: <u>Not applicable</u>

- PR interval: <u>Not applicable</u>

- QRS: <u>0.24 seconds</u>

- QT interval: <u>Not applicable</u>

- Underlying rhythm: <u>Ventricular tachycardia</u>

- Variant: <u>Ventricular tachycardia</u>

- Interpretation: <u>Ventricular tachycardia</u>

- Treatment: <u>Determine responsiveness of the patient. If the patient is conscious, apply</u>
  <u>oxygen and treat with intravenous amiodarone or lidocaine following ACLS protocols.</u>
  <u>If the patient is conscious but unstable (i.e., has a low blood pressure and symptoms</u>
  <u>of decompensation), synchronized cardioversion may be needed to terminate the</u>
  <u>rhythm (Diehl, 2011; Marcum, 2013).</u>
  <u>   If the patient is unconscious, the dysrhythmia must be treated as if it is</u>
  <u>ventricular fibrillation. The patient is effectively in cardiac arrest. The ACLS protocol</u>
  <u>must be instituted immediately. CPR must be initiated and the patient defibrillated</u>
  <u>as soon as possible (Sinz, 2011).</u>

- Discussion

  - **Rate:** There are no P waves so there is no atrial rate. The ventricular rate is
    130 bpm.
  - **Rhythm:** The rhythm is regular.
  - **P wave origin and PR interval:** These are not available here because there are no
    P waves.
  - **QRS:** To be honest, this strip is hard to read. The boxes are hard to see, but it's
    not rocket science to determine that these are wide. I could read the boxes well
    enough to estimate that they were 0.24 wide, but I really do not care. If they are
    wide, they are wide, and that makes the diagnosis. There are no P waves and
    the QRS complexes are wide. That makes this ventricular in origin. Because the
    complexes make a rhythm and the rhythm is greater than 100 bpm, then this is a
    tachycardia that is of ventricular origin, or VT.

EKG 4.18

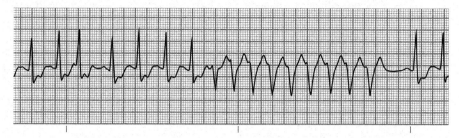

- Rate: Atrial <u>50 bpm</u> Ventricular <u>140 bpm</u>
- Rhythm: Irregular
- P wave origin: <u>SA node</u>
- PR interval: <u>0.16 seconds</u>
- QRS: <u>0.12/0.20 seconds</u>
- QT interval: <u>Not applicable</u>
- Underlying rhythm: <u>Sinus tachycardia versus atrial tachycardia</u>
- Variant: <u>Nine-beat run of ventricular tachycardia</u>
- Interpretation: <u>Sinus tachycardia with a nine-beat run of V-tach</u>
- Treatment: <u>No matter the origin, if the ventricular tachycardia is not stopped, or does not spontaneously stop (as it does in this rhythm), it will eventually deteriorate into ventricular fibrillation. If the patient is awake, however, and there is blood pumping to the brain, there is time to treat this dysrhythmia with oxygen and with intravenous amiodarone or lidocaine following ACLS protocols. If the patient is conscious but unstable (i.e., has a low blood pressure and symptoms of decompensation), synchronized cardioversion may be needed to terminate the rhythm</u> (Diehl, 2011; Marcum, 2013).

  <u>If the patient is unconscious, the dysrhythmia must be treated as if it is ventricular fibrillation. The patient is effectively in cardiac arrest. The ACLS protocol must be instituted immediately. CPR must be initiated and the patient defibrillated as soon as possible.</u>

- Discussion

  - **Rate:** I can count P waves in these beats, but it is tricky. It is tricky because the rate is so rapid that the P waves and T waves are, sometime, bumping into each other. However, since the T waves do not look exactly alike, there must be something causing that distortion. The only thing that can do that is a P wave.
  - **Rhythm:** The rhythm is irregular because beat #3 comes in early, but that is the least of my concern. The rhythm between beats 1 and 2, 4 and 5, 5 and 6, and 6 and 7 are consistent. The rhythm between beats 8 and 16 is also consistent but not the same as the previous rhythm.
  - **P wave origin:** This is not an easy strip, and it is used to demonstrate where clinical judgement is needed. The P waves are difficult to see except in the fourth beat. It is very clear and certainly sinus in origin. In beats 1, 2, 5, 6, and 7, it is very difficult to see the P waves. That is because the rate is so rapid that the P waves and

the preceding T waves are bumping into each other. I can tell that because the T waves of the preceding beats all look just a little different. All T waves should look the same. If they do not, there must be something causing them to be distorted. The only thing between the T wave and the next QRS complex is the P wave. Because I can see the P wave clearly in beat #4, and because the rhythm between those beats is regular, I can assume that the P waves are from the SA node. If I am a purist and argue that I cannot make that assumption because I cannot see the other P waves clearly, then this is at least an atrial tachycardia. The reason that I can see the P wave so clearly in #4 is because beat #3 is actually premature and creates a little space between it and #4.

- **QRS:** The QRS widths are normal in beats 1–7, and P waves are there indicating a supraventricular (above the ventricle) origin. Beats 8–16 are wide and bizarre looking indicating a ventricular origin. The questions is whether or not there is blood being pumped. Depending on where the VT is originating, contraction can be "near normal" allowing blood to be pumped, or reversed so that no blood is pumped. If there is no blood being pumped, the patient will be clinically dead and the rhythm treated as ventricular fibrillation. Fortunately for this patient, the ventricular tachycardia terminated spontaneously.

EKG 4.19

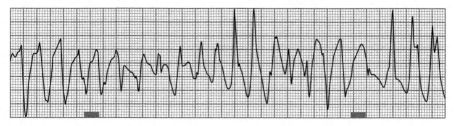

Source: Green, J. M., & Chiaramida, A. J. (2015). *12-Lead EKG confidence* (3rd ed., p. 161). New York, NY: Springer Publishing.

- Rate: Atrial <u>0</u> Ventricular <u>Greater than 200 bpm</u>

- Rhythm: Irregular

- P wave origin: <u>Not applicable</u>

- PR interval: <u>Not applicable</u>

- QRS: <u>Not applicable</u>

- QT interval: <u>Not applicable</u>

- Underlying rhythm: <u>Ventricular tachycardia</u>

- Variant: <u>Bow tie configuration</u>

- Interpretation: <u>Torsades de Pointes</u>

- Treatment: <u>Prevent by checking and correcting electrolyte abnormalities. Discontinue medications that can prolong the QT interval. Treat with intravenous (IV) magnesium, isoproterenol, or phenytoin along with electrocardioversion if needed (Bucher, 2014; Diehl, 2011; Marcum, 2013; Sinz, 2011). Determine responsiveness of the patient. If the patient is unconscious, the dysrhythmia must be treated as if it is ventricular fibrillation. The patient is effectively in cardiac arrest. The ACLS protocol must be instituted immediately. CPR must be initiated, and the patient defibrillated as soon as possible (Sinz, 2011).</u>

- Discussion: Torsades de Pointes is a specialized VT that is associated with prolonged QT intervals (Bucher, 2014; Diehl, 2011; Marcum, 2013; Sinz, 2011). It is often caused by magnesium deficiencies and may be prevented by ensuring that magnesium levels are within normal ranges. It is characterized by ventricular complexes that change in configuration and usually create a "bow tie" effect on the monitor. This is a lethal arrhythmia that should be treated as pulseless VT. Because it is a lethal arrhythmia, prevention is preferable to treatment.

EKG 4.20

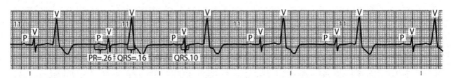

Source: Green, J. M., & Chiaramida, A. J. (2015). *12-Lead EKG confidence* (3rd ed., p. 149). New York, NY: Springer Publishing.

- Rate: Atrial <u>30 to 40 bpm</u> Ventricular <u>80 bpm</u>

- Rhythm: Irregular due to premature beats

- P wave origin: <u>SA node</u>

- PR interval: <u>0.26 seconds</u>

- QRS: <u>0.10 seconds and 0.16 seconds</u>

- QT interval: <u>Not applicable</u>

- Underlying rhythm: <u>Sinus rhythm with first-degree heart block</u>

- Variant: <u>Every other beat is a premature ventricular contraction</u>

- Interpretation: <u>Sinus rhythm with first-degree heart block and bigeminal PVCs</u>

- Treatment: <u>The first order of treatment would be to administer oxygen. Electrolyte levels, especially potassium and magnesium, need to be examined and treated if necessary (Bucher, 20014; Diehl, 2011). Medications, such as amiodarone, procainamide, lidocaine, and/or beta-adrenergic blockers, can be used for control of PVCs (Bucher, 2014; Diehl, 2011).</u>

- Discussion

  - **Rate:** There are three P waves giving an atrial rate of 30 beats per minute (3 × 10). There was one P wave just outside of the first marker that would make the rate 40 bpm if I chose to count it. However, there are eight QRS complexes giving a ventricular rate of 80 beats per minute.
  - **Rhythm:** The rhythm is irregular due to the premature beats.
  - **P wave origin:** The P waves are all the same in configuration and are probably the patient's normal P waves, so the assumption is that they are coming from the SA node. The premature beats, however, have no P waves associated with them.
  - **PR interval:** The PR interval (when present) is longer than normal (0.26), indicating the presence of a first-degree heart block.
  - **QRS:** The QRS complexes that have P waves are normal in configuration and width. The premature beats are wide. Wide complexes that have no P waves are usually coming from the ventricles, so these are PVCs. The PVCs are coming in a definite pattern (every other beat), making this bigeminy.

EKG 4.21

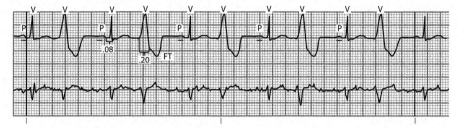

- Rate: Atrial <u>50 bpm</u> Ventricular <u>100 bpm</u>
- Rhythm: Irregular due to early beats
- P wave origin: <u>SA node</u>
- PR interval: <u>0.16 seconds</u>
- QRS: <u>0.08 seconds and 0.20 seconds</u>
- QT interval: <u>Not applicable</u>
- Underlying rhythm: <u>Sinus</u>
- Variant: <u>Every other beat is a premature ventricular contraction</u>
- Interpretation: <u>Sinus rhythm with bigeminal PVCs</u>
- Treatment: <u>Bigeminal PVCs may indicate increasing ventricular irritability (Diehl, 2011) and increase the risk of lethal arrhythmias such as ventricular tachycardia or ventricular fibrillation. The first order of treatment would be to administer oxygen. Electrolyte levels, especially potassium and magnesium, need to be examined and treated if necessary (Bucher, 2014; Diehl, 2011). Medications, such as amiodarone, procainamide, lidocaine, and/or beta-adrenergic blockers, can be used for control of PVCs (Bucher, 2014; Diehl, 2011).</u>
- Discussion
  - **Rate and Rhythm:** There are 5 P waves between the first and third "3 second" markers giving an atrial rate of 50. However, every other beat comes early and has no P wave causing an irregular rhythm.
  - **P waves and PR interval:** The P waves are all consistent in appearance and the PR interval is also consistent indicating that the P waves are coming from the SA node.
  - **QRS:** The QRS complexes that are preceded by P waves are all narrow indicating that they are traveling down normal conductive pathways. Every other beat, however, is wide with the T wave going opposite of the main complex direction indicating a ventricular origin. Since every other beat is ventricular, the pattern is bigeminal.

EKG 4.22

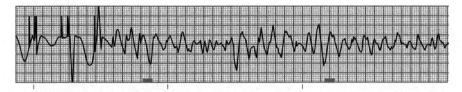

Source: Green, J. M., & Chiaramida, A. J. (2015). *12-Lead EKG confidence* (3rd ed., p. 170). New York, NY: Springer Publishing.

- Rate: Atrial <u>0</u> Ventricular <u>0</u>

- Rhythm: Not applicable

- P wave origin: <u>Not applicable</u>

- PR interval: <u>Not applicable</u>

- QRS: <u>Not applicable</u>

- QT interval: <u>Not applicable</u>

- Underlying rhythm: <u>Ventricular fibrillation</u>

- Variant: <u>Coarse</u>

- Interpretation: <u>Coarse ventricular fibrillation</u>

- Treatment: <u>Assess the patient. If the patient is awake or breathing, he or she is not in ventricular fibrillation. Check the patient's leads. If the patient is unresponsive, begin CPR and call for help. Institute ACLS protocols as soon as possible.</u>

- Discussion: It is important to understand that the heart is not pumping blood, but that does not mean that the heart is not working. It is working very hard, but it is not working in a coordinated fashion. Something has happened to cause all of the cells in the heart to depolarize and repolarize randomly. The end result is a lot of work being done, but the lack of coordination and cooperation leads to no effective end result or heart contraction.

    The fact that "work" is being done leads to resources being used up. Oxygen and glucose are being used. Without blood flow, no more resources (oxygen and glucose) are being brought in. In the meantime, waste is being produced and there is no blood flow to carry the waste away from the heart tissue.

    In approximately 90 seconds (1½ minutes), the heart will be so toxic that it will not be able to respond to electrical shock. However, there is a solution. Oxygen must be replaced, and toxic waste must be removed. Blood flow and oxygen supply must be restored. The key to that is CPR.

    CPR will not convert ventricular fibrillation back into a sinus rhythm. Only defibrillation will do that. The only way out of "V-fib" is to "D-fib." However, CPR will provide circulation and oxygenation enough to buy you time so that defibrillation will be successful.

    When ventricular fibrillation first starts, the rhythm is "coarse" looking. As time goes on, the rhythm will become finer and finer until it becomes a straight line. The progressive deterioration of the rhythm (as the rhythm becomes "finer") indicates the increasing level of toxicity in the heart muscle. This is of great concern because the more toxic the muscle is, the less likely it is that it will respond to defibrillation. Fortunately, there is a medication that has the unique ability to convert fine fibrillation back into coarse fibrillation.

Epinephrine (Adrenalin) is that medication. Epinephrine is a catecholamine that is also a potent vasoconstrictor that has a very short duration (Comerford, 2016). It is possible that the sudden constriction of the coronary arteries may force "toxic" blood out of the heart and then the relaxation of the arteries soon afterward may "suck" oxygenated blood in. In that way, it can convert the fine fibrillation back to coarse fibrillation. For that reason, this medication is given every 3 to 5 minutes during a cardiac arrest (code) situation.

Again, epinephrine will not break the rhythm. It will only make it more susceptible to defibrillation. However, the cause of the fibrillation is still not known and may never be known, so antiarrhythmics are used to prevent the heart from going back into fibrillation once defibrillation successfully terminates the fibrillation. Amiodarone and lidocaine are two of those antiarrhythmic medications. Use per ACLS protocols.

EKG 4.23

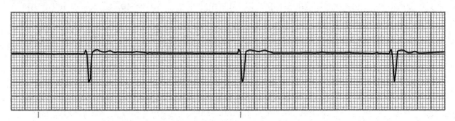

- Rate: Atrial <u>0</u> Ventricular <u>30 bpm</u>
- Rhythm: Regular
- P wave origin: <u>Not applicable</u>
- PR interval: <u>Not applicable</u>
- QRS: <u>0.14 seconds</u>
- QT interval: <u>Not applicable</u>
- Underlying rhythm: <u>Ventricular</u>
- Variant: <u>Ventricular rhythm</u>
- Interpretation: <u>Idioventricular rhythm</u>
- Treatment: <u>Ideally, it would be nice to replace this with a rhythm coming from the SA node. The medication of choice to do that would be atropine (Diehl, 2011; Sinz, 2011). Epinephrine or dopamine may also be used if atropine is not effective (Sinz, 2011). When the rhythm is refractory to medication therapy, transcutaneous pacing may be advisable until a transvenous pacemaker can be placed (Diehl, 2011; Sinz, 2011). BCLS and ACLS may be required if the patient is not tolerating this rhythm (Sinz, 2011). Do not try to suppress this rhythm using antiarrhythmic drugs such as amiodarone or lidocaine. The result would be no rhythm at all.</u>
- Discussion
  - **Rate and Rhythm:** There are no P waves here so the atrial rate is 0. The ventricular rate is 30 bpm and the ventricular rhythm is regular. This would suggest an idioventricular rhythm.
  - **PR interval and QRS complex:** Since there are no P waves, there is no PR interval. The QRS complex is wide indicate a ventricular origin.

EKG 4.24

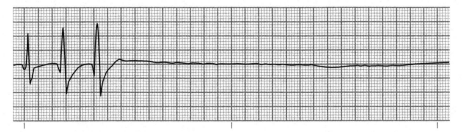

- Rate: Atrial <u>0</u> Ventricular <u>0</u>
- Rhythm: Irregular
- P wave origin: <u>Not applicable</u>
- PR interval: <u>Not applicable</u>
- QRS: <u>Wide but variable</u>
- QT interval: <u>Not applicable</u>
- Underlying rhythm: <u>Ventricular tachycardia</u>
- Variant: <u>Ventricular standstill (cardiac arrest)</u>
- Interpretation: <u>Cardiac arrest</u>
- Treatment: <u>Check the patient. If he or she is breathing, do not initiate CPR. Check the patient's leads. If one wire fell off, it could mimic this rhythm. If the patient is non-responsive, this could be asystole. The fact is, if someone is truly asystolic, there is no hope. Nothing is going to bring this person back. He or she is dead. If that is the attitude, then why try? If you have resigned yourself to this thought process, you have condemned your patient to death. There is, however, another way to look at this.</u>
  <u>What if this is not asystole? What if, instead, this is a very fine ventricular fibrillation? We can treat ventricular fibrillation. If we think of asystole as a fine ventricular fibrillation, then our goal will be to convert the fine fibrillation to a coarse fibrillation so that we can defibrillate with a better chance of success. The drug of choice to do this is epinephrine (Adrenalin). Epinephrine, however, will not work unless we get circulation going, so CPR is required followed by ACLS.</u>

- Discussion
  - **Rate and Rhythm:** There are no P waves. There are 3 QRS complexes, but that becomes irrelevant when the patient goes "flatline."
  - **QRS:** The QRS complexes that are present are wide and ventricular in origin. They are also rapid until there are no more. This could be cardiac arrest. Check the patient and the electrodes while preparing to initiate BCLS and ACLS protocols.

Answers to Chapter 5: Paced Rhythms

EKG 5.1

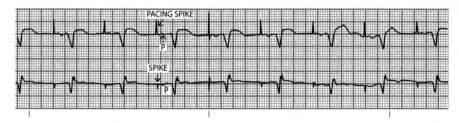

- Rate: Atrial <u>70 beats per minute (bpm)</u> Ventricular <u>70 bpm</u>
- Rhythm: Regular
- P wave origin: <u>Paced</u>
- PR interval: <u>Consistent</u>
- QRS: <u>0.12 seconds</u>
- QT interval: <u>Not applicable</u>
- Underlying rhythm: <u>Atrial paced</u>
- Variant: <u>Not applicable</u>
- Interpretation: <u>Atrial paced 100%</u>
- Treatment: <u>Not applicable</u>
- Discussion
  - **Rate:** There are seven P waves (although they are small) and seven QRS complexes giving atrial and ventricular rates of 70 bpm.
  - **Rhythm:** The rhythm is regular.
  - **P wave origin:** There is a pacing spike before each P wave, indicating that the source of the P wave is the pacing spike.
  - **PR interval:** As is common with paced rhythms, the PR interval is consistent.
  - **QRS:** The QRS width is within normal limits.

EKG 5.2

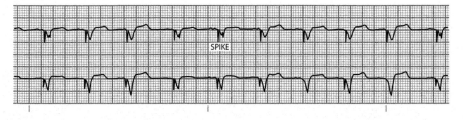

SPIKE

- Rate: Atrial <u>0</u> Ventricular <u>90 bpm</u>
- Rhythm: Regular
- P wave origin: <u>Not applicable</u>
- PR interval: <u>Not applicable</u>
- QRS: <u>0.12 seconds</u>
- QT interval: <u>Not applicable</u>
- Underlying rhythm: <u>Ventricular pacing</u>
- Variant: <u>Not applicable</u>
- Interpretation: <u>Ventricular pacing 100%</u>
- Treatment: <u>Not applicable</u>
- Discussion
  - **Rate:** There are no P waves, so there is no atrial rate. There are nine QRS complexes, indicating a rate of 90 bpm.
  - **Rhythm:** The rhythm is regular, which is usually the case with rhythms that are 100% paced.
  - **P wave origin and PR interval:** These do not exist as there is no P wave.
  - **QRS:** Each QRS is preceded by a pacing spike, indicating that this rhythm is ventricularly paced. Because there are no natural or "intrinsic" complexes, the patient is being paced 100% of the time.

EKG 5.3

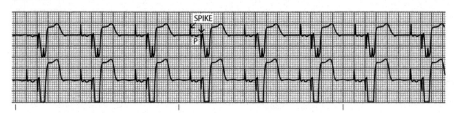

- Rate: Atrial <u>60 bpm</u> Ventricular <u>60 bpm</u>
- Rhythm: Regular
- P wave origin: <u>Atrial paced</u>
- PR interval: <u>0.20 seconds</u>
- QRS: <u>0.16 seconds</u>
- QT interval: <u>Not applicable</u>
- Underlying rhythm: <u>Atrial paced/ventricular paced</u>
- Variant: <u>Not applicable</u>
- Interpretation: <u>Atrioventricular pacing 100%</u>
- Treatment: <u>Not applicable</u>
- Discussion
    - **Rate:** There are six P waves and six QRS complexes, indicating that both the atria and ventricles are producing at a rate of 60 bpm.
    - **Rhythm:** The rhythm is regular as would be expected with a 100% paced rhythm.
    - **P wave origin:** There is a pacing spike before each P wave, indicating that the pacemaker is the source of the P wave.
    - **PR interval:** This is consistent at 0.20 seconds.
    - **QRS:** Each QRS has a pacing spike before it, indicating that the ventricles are being paced 100%. The QRS is wide at 0.16 seconds (>0.12), but this is expected because a paced beat is artificially created and probably is originating in muscle tissue instead of conductive tissue.
    - **Interpretation:** Because both of these show pacing spikes before both the P waves and the QRS complexes, this would be an atrial/ventricular (AV) pacemaker pacing 100% of the time.

EKG 5.4

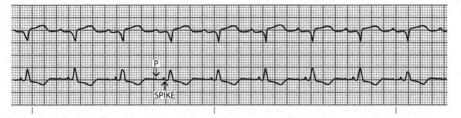

- Rate: Atrial <u>80 bpm</u> Ventricular <u>80 bpm</u>
- Rhythm: Regular
- P wave origin: <u>SA node</u>
- PR interval: <u>0.16 seconds</u>
- QRS: <u>0.10 seconds</u>
- QT interval: <u>0.40 seconds (R-R interval = 0.80 seconds)</u>
- Underlying rhythm: <u>Sinus</u>
- Variant: <u>Ventricular pacing</u>
- Interpretation: <u>Atrial sensing/ventricular pacing 100%</u>
- Treatment: <u>Not applicable</u>
- Discussion
    - **Rate:** There are eight P waves and eight QRS complexes, indicating that the atrial and ventricular rates are both 80 bpm. Granted, the P waves are hard to see in the bottom rhythm, but they are clear in the top rhythm. By the same token, the pacing spikes are hard to see in the top rhythm, but quite clear in the bottom. This is the beauty of having two leads.
    - **Rhythm:** The rhythm is regular.
    - **P wave origin:** The P waves are consistent in appearance and are assumed to be the patient's normal. This would lead to the assumption that the source of these P waves would be the sinoatrial (SA) node.
    - **PR interval:** The PR interval is within normal limits.
    - **QRS:** There is a pacing spike before each QRS complex, indicating that the pacemaker is the source of the QRS complexes and that the ventricles are being paced.
    - **Interpretation:** Because the PR interval is consistent, the assumption is that the ventricles are being "told" when to depolarize, with the P wave being the timing trigger. The pacemaker, then, must be sensing the atrial activity and then pacing the ventricle at the proper time. This is atrial sensing and ventricular pacing.

EKG 5.5

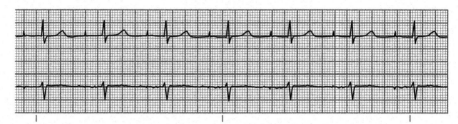

- Rate: Atrial <u>60 bpm</u> Ventricular <u>60 bpm</u>

- Rhythm: Regular

- P wave origin: <u>Paced</u>

- PR interval: <u>0.28 seconds</u>

- QRS: <u>0.10 seconds</u>

- QT interval: <u>0.44 seconds (R-R interval = 0.96 seconds)</u>

- Underlying rhythm: <u>Atrial paced</u>

- Variant: <u>Pacer spikes before P waves</u>

- Interpretation: <u>100% atrial paced</u>

- Treatment: <u>None</u>

- Discussion

  - **Rate:** There are six P waves and six QRS complexes, indicating a rate of 60 bpm for both the atria and the ventricles. (Let's be honest. These P waves are very difficult to see. It might even take a little imagination, but this is not uncommon with atrial pacemakers. They are a little bit clearer in the last two complexes but still hard to see. Often, if the pacer spikes are consistent and everything else is okay, we assume that the P waves are there. This lead should actually be changed and manipulated until the P waves can be more clearly defined.)
  - **Rhythm:** The rhythm is regular.
  - **P wave origin:** There is a pacing spike before each very small P wave, indicating that the pacemaker is the source of the P wave.
  - **PR interval:** The PR interval is a bit long here, indicating that there may be some issue with the AV node as well, but it is also difficult to see where the P wave actually starts. There may be a little delay between the pacing and the capture. At any rate, something to watch, but nothing to panic over.
  - **QRS:** There are no pacer spikes preceding the QRS complexes, and the complex widths are within normal limits.
  - **Interpretation:** The atria are being paced. Even though the P waves are so small, the consistent PR interval strongly suggests that an impulse is traveling through the AV node and causing depolarization of the ventricles. This is 100% atrial pacing.

EKG 5.6

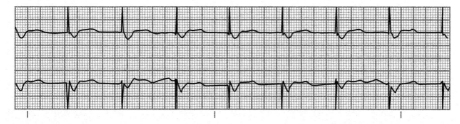

- Rate: Atrial <u>0</u> Ventricular <u>70 bpm</u>

- Rhythm: Regular

- P wave origin: <u>None</u>

- PR interval: <u>Not applicable</u>

- QRS: <u>Wide</u>

- QT interval: <u>Not applicable</u>

- Underlying rhythm: <u>Ventricular paced</u>

- Variant: <u>Not applicable</u>

- Interpretation: <u>Ventricular pacing 100%</u>

- Treatment: <u>Not applicable</u>

- Discussion

  - **Rate:** There are no P waves or atrial pacing spikes. There are seven QRS complexes in 6 seconds, indicating a rate of 70 bpm.
  - **Rhythm:** The rhythm is regular.
  - **P wave origin; PR interval:** Because there are no P waves, there is no P wave origin or PR interval.
  - **QRS:** There is a pacing spike before each QRS complex. The QRS complexes are wide, but that is not uncommon with paced complexes because the pacing most likely occurs in the muscle portion of the ventricle, instead of the normal conductive pathway.

EKG 5.7

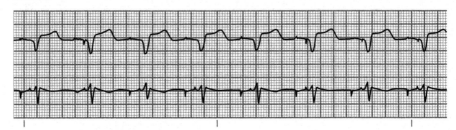

- Rate: Atrial <u>70 bpm</u> Ventricular <u>70 bpm</u>
- Rhythm: Regular
- P wave origin: <u>Atrial paced</u>
- PR interval: <u>0.16 seconds</u>
- QRS: <u>0.14 seconds</u>
- QT interval: <u>Not applicable</u>
- Underlying rhythm: <u>Atrial pacing</u>
- Variant: <u>Ventricular pacing</u>
- Interpretation: <u>Atrioventricular pacing 100%</u>
- Treatment: <u>Not applicable</u>
- Discussion
  - **Rate:** There are seven P waves and seven QRS complexes in the 6-second strip, indicating a rate of 70 bpm for both the atria and the ventricles.
  - **Rhythm:** The rhythm is regular.
  - **P wave origin:** There is a pacing spike before each P wave, indicating that the pacemaker is the source of atrial stimulation.
  - **PR interval:** This is normal at 0.16 and is preset in this type of pacemaker (the ventricular electrode is set to fire at a certain time after the atrial electrode).
  - **QRS:** There is a pacing spike before each QRS complex, indicating that the pacemaker is the source of QRS generation. The complexes are slightly wider than normal due to the placement of the ventricular electrode onto muscle instead of the normal conductive tissue of the ventricle.
  - **Interpretation:** Both the atria and the ventricles are being paced 100% of the time.

EKG 5.8

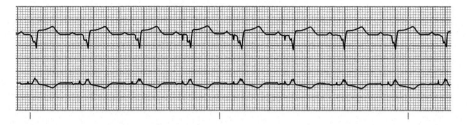

- Rate: Atrial <u>70 bpm</u> Ventricular <u>70 bpm</u>
- Rhythm: Regular
- P wave origin: <u>SA node</u>
- PR interval: <u>0.14 seconds</u>
- QRS: <u>0.10 seconds</u>
- QT interval: <u>Not applicable</u>
- Underlying rhythm: <u>Sinus</u>
- Variant: <u>Ventricular pacing</u>
- Interpretation: <u>Atrial sensing/ventricular pacing 100%</u>
- Treatment: <u>Not applicable</u>
- Discussion
    - **Rate:** There are seven P waves and seven QRS complexes, indicating that the atrial and ventricular rates are both 70 bpm.
    - **Rhythm:** The rhythm is regular.
    - **P wave origin:** The P waves are consistent in appearance and are assumed to be the patient's normal. This would lead to the assumption that the source of these P waves would be the SA node.
    - **PR interval:** The PR interval is within normal limits.
    - **QRS:** There is a pacing spike before each QRS complex, indicating that the pacemaker is the source of the QRS complexes and that the ventricles are being paced.
    - **Interpretation:** Because the PR interval is consistent, the assumption is that the ventricles are being "told" when to depolarize, with the P wave being the timing trigger. The pacemaker, then, must be sensing the atrial activity and then pacing the ventricle at the proper time. This is atrial sensing and ventricular pacing.

EKG 5.9

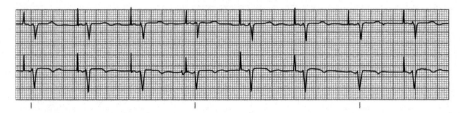

- Rate: Atrial <u>70 bpm</u> Ventricular <u>70 bpm</u>
- Rhythm: Regular
- P wave origin: <u>Atrial paced</u>
- PR interval: <u>0.14 seconds</u>
- QRS: <u>0.10 seconds</u>
- QT interval: <u>Not applicable</u>
- Underlying rhythm: <u>Atrial paced</u>
- Variant: <u>Not applicable</u>
- Interpretation: <u>Atrial paced 100%</u>
- Treatment: <u>Not applicable</u>
- Discussion

  - **Rate:** There are seven P waves and seven QRS complexes, indicating a rate of 70 bpm for both the atria and the ventricles.
  - **Rhythm:** The rhythm is regular.
  - **P wave origin:** There is a pacing spike before each P wave, indicating that the pacemaker is the source of the P wave.
  - **PR interval:** The PR interval is within normal limits.
  - **QRS:** There are no pacer spikes preceding the QRS complexes, and the complex widths are within normal limits.
  - **Interpretation:** The atria are being paced. The consistent PR interval strongly suggests that an impulse is traveling through the AV node and causing depolarization of the ventricles. This is 100% atrial pacing.

EKG 5.10

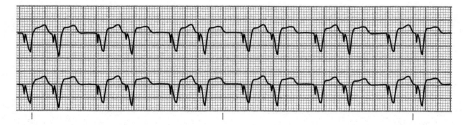

- Rate: Atrial 0 Ventricular 100 bpm
- Rhythm: Irregular
- P wave origin: None
- PR interval: Not applicable
- QRS: 0.14 seconds
- QT interval: Not applicable
- Underlying rhythm: Ventricular pacing
- Variant: Irregular rhythm
- Interpretation: Ventricular pacing 100%
- Treatment: Not applicable
- Discussion
   - **Rate:** There are no P waves or atrial pacing spikes. There are 10 QRS complexes in 6 seconds, indicating a rate of 100 bpm.
   - **Rhythm:** The rhythm is irregular.
   - **P wave origin/PR interval:** Because there are no P waves, there is no P wave origin or PR interval.
   - **QRS:** There is a pacing spike before each QRS complex. The QRS complexes are wide, but that is not uncommon with paced complexes as the pacing most likely occurs in the muscle portion of the ventricle instead of the normal conductive pathway. What is bothersome is the irregularity of the rhythm. It is irregular, but does appear to have a pattern. I may be tempted to query the provider for a rationale for why.

EKG 5.11

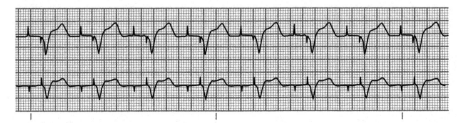

- Rate: Atrial <u>70 bpm</u> Ventricular <u>70 bpm</u>
- Rhythm: Regular
- P wave origin: <u>Atrial paced</u>
- PR interval: <u>0.20 seconds</u>
- QRS: <u>0.18 seconds</u>
- QT interval: <u>Not applicable</u>
- Underlying rhythm: <u>Atrial pacing</u>
- Variant: <u>Ventricular pacing</u>
- Interpretation: <u>AV pacing 100%</u>
- Treatment: <u>Not applicable</u>
- Note: Notice how small the P waves are. They can barely be seen. This is common with AV pacing, and the leads may need to be manipulated to get the best view of the P wave possible.

- Discussion

  - **Rate:** There are seven P waves and seven QRS complexes, indicating a rate of 70 bpm for both the atria and the ventricles. (Let's be honest. These P waves are very difficult to see. It might even take a little imagination, but this is not uncommon with atrial pacemakers. They are a little bit clearer in the last two complexes, but still hard to see. Often, if the pacer spikes are consistent and everything else is okay, we assume that the P waves are there. This lead should actually be changed and manipulated until the P waves can be more clearly defined.)
  - **Rhythm:** The rhythm is regular.
  - **P wave origin:** There is a pacing spike before each very small P wave, indicating that the pacemaker is the source of the P wave.
  - **PR interval:** The PR interval is a bit long here, but it is also difficult to see where the P wave actually starts. There may be a little delay between the pacing and the capture. At any rate, this is something to watch, but not to panic over.
  - **QRS:** There are pacer spikes preceding each of the QRS complexes, and the complex widths are wide, probably due to electrode placement on cardiac muscle instead of the normal conductive pathways.
  - **Interpretation:** The atria are being paced and so are the ventricles. This is 100% atrial–ventricular pacing.

EKG 5.12

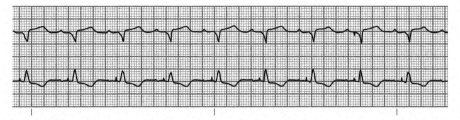

- Rate: Atrial <u>70 bpm</u> Ventricular <u>70 bpm</u>
- Rhythm: Regular
- P wave origin: <u>SA node</u>
- PR interval: <u>0.20 seconds</u>
- QRS: <u>0.10 seconds</u>
- QT interval: <u>Not applicable</u>
- Underlying rhythm: <u>Sinus</u>
- Variant: <u>Ventricular pacing</u>
- Interpretation: <u>Atrial sensing/ventricular pacing 100%</u>
- Treatment: <u>Not applicable</u>
- Note: Note how small the pacemaker spike is. It is only visible on the lower rhythm.
- Discussion
  - **Rate:** There are seven P waves and seven QRS complexes, indicating that the atrial and ventricular rates are both 70 bpm.
  - **Rhythm:** The rhythm is regular.
  - **P wave origin:** The P waves are consistent in appearance and are assumed to be the patient's normal rhythm. This would lead to the assumption that the source of these P waves is the SA node.
  - **PR interval:** The PR interval is within normal limits.
  - **QRS:** There is a pacing spike before each QRS complex, indicating that the pacemaker is the source of the QRS complexes and that the ventricles are being paced.
  - **Interpretation:** Because the PR interval is consistent, the assumption is that the ventricles are being "told" when to depolarize, with the P wave being the timing trigger. The pacemaker, then, must be sensing the atrial activity and then pacing the ventricle at the proper time. This is atrial sensing and ventricular pacing.

Answers to Chapter 6: 12-Lead EKGs

EKG 6.1

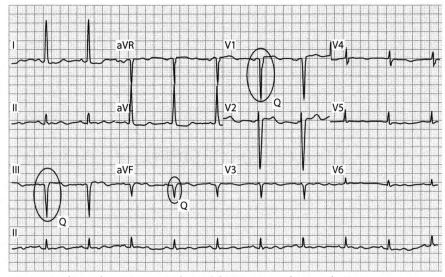

aVF, augmented vector foot; aVL, augmented vector left; aVR, augmented vector right; V, vector.

I	aVR	V1	V4
Q No	Q___	Q Yes	Q No
ST Slight depression	ST___	ST Slight elevation	ST Isoelectric
T Upright	T___	T Upright	T Isoelectric
II	aVL	V2	V5
Q No	Q No	Q No	Q No
ST Isoelectric	ST Slight depression	ST Slight elevation	ST Isoelectric
T Upright	T Upright	T Upright	T Isoelectric
III	aVF	V3	V6
Q Yes	Q Yes	Q No	Q No
ST Slight elevation	ST Slight elevation	ST Isoelectric	ST Isoelectric
T Biphasic	T Biphasic	T Biphasic	T Isoelectric

■ Axis: Left axis deviation

- Interpretation: There are significant Q waves in leads III and aVF (augmented vector foot), indicating the presence of an inferior wall myocardial infarction (MI). The ST segments are only slightly elevated, making determination of the age of the infarction difficult. The T wave abnormalities, however, do indicate that something has happened. The left axis shift would lend support to the theory that there has been damage to the right side of the heart. There is also a Q wave with slight ST elevation in V1, but no other significant anterior lead changes are shown so the Q wave in V1 is not an indicator of MI.

- Diagnosis: This is an inferior wall MI; age undetermined.

EKG 6.2

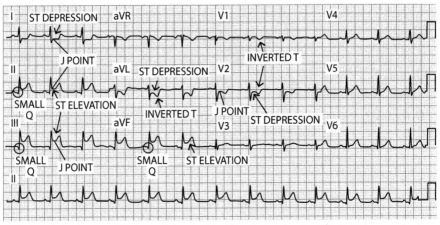

aVF, augmented vector foot; aVL, augmented vector left; aVR, augmented vector right; V, vector.

I	aVR	V1	V4
Q No	Q ___	Q No	Q No
ST Depressed	ST ___	ST Isoelectric	ST Isoelectric
T Upright	T ___	T Inverted	T Upright
II	aVL	V2	V5
Q Small	Q No	Q No	Q No
ST Elevated	ST Depressed	ST Depressed	ST Isoelectric
T Upright	T Inverted	T Inverted	T Upright
III	aVF	V3	V6
Q Small	Q Small	Q No	Q Small
ST Elevated	ST Elevated	ST Isoelectric	ST Isoelectric
T Upright	T Upright	T Isoelectric	T Upright

- Axis: Normal axis deviation

- Interpretation: There is significant ST elevation (ischemia) in leads II, III, and aVF with small and (at this point) insignificant Q waves. This is possibly an evolving inferior wall MI. At any rate, the ischemia in the inferior wall places the patient at risk for arrhythmia and sudden death. There is also ST depression in leads I and augmented vector left (aVL), which could indicate lateral wall ischemia as well.

- Diagnosis: The patient has inferolateral wall ischemia with probable evolution of inferior MI.

EKG 6.3

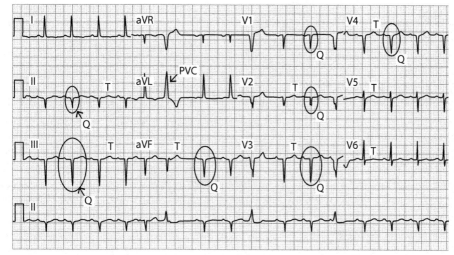

aVF, augmented vector foot; aVL, augmented vector left; aVR, augmented vector right; PVC, premature ventricular contraction; V, vector.

I	aVR	V1	V4
Q No	Q____	Q Yes	Q Yes
ST Isoelectric	ST____	ST Isoelectric	ST Isoelectric
T Inverted	T____	T Flat	T Upright
II	aVL	V2	V5
Q Yes	Q No	Q Yes	Q No
ST Isoelectric	ST Isoelectric	ST Isoelectric	ST Isoelectric
T Upright	T Flat	T Upright	T Upright
III	aVF	V3	V6
Q Yes	Q Yes	Q Yes	Q No
ST Isoelectric	ST Isoelectric	ST Isoelectric	ST Isoelectric
T Upright	T Upright	T Upright	T Upright

- Axis: Left axis deviation

- Interpretation: There are significant Q waves is leads II, III, aVF, V1, V2, V3, and V4, indicating MIs in the inferior and anterior walls. However, there are no ST elevations or depressions shown anywhere to cause these MIs, so they must be old.

- Diagnosis: Old anterior and old inferior wall MIs are present.

EKG 6.4

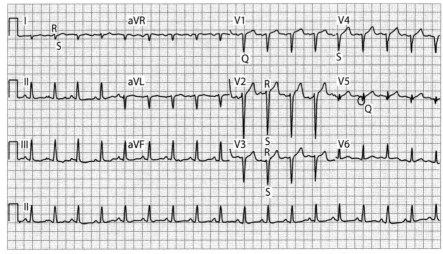

aVF, augmented vector foot; aVL, augmented vector left; aVR, augmented vector right; V, vector.

I	aVR	V1	V4
Q No	Q____	Q Yes	Q No
ST Isoelectric	ST____	ST Isoelectric	ST Slightly elevated
T Isoelectric	T____	T Upright	T Upright
II	aVL	V2	V5
Q No	Q No	Q No	Q Yes
ST Slightly depressed	ST Isoelectric	ST Slightly elevated	ST Isoelectric
T Isoelectric	T Isoelectric	T Upright	T Upright
III	aVF	V3	V6
Q No	Q No	Q No	Q No
ST Isoelectric	ST Isoelectric	ST Slightly elevated	ST Isoelectric
T Isoelectric	T Isoelectric	T Upright	T Upright

- Axis: Right axis deviation

- Interpretation: Leads V1 and V5 both show a significant Q wave, but they are not related leads so those Q waves mean nothing. There are no other significant Q waves, so no heart attack has occurred. There are some ST elevations in lead V2 and possibly V3 but very slight. Although the elevations are not very high, they are all in the anterior leads. The right axis deviation is expected when there is left-sided heart damage making this EKG suspicious.

- Diagnosis: Anterior wall ischemia is present.

EKG 6.5

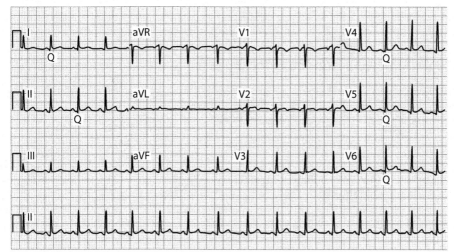

aVF, augmented vector foot; aVL, augmented vector left; aVR, augmented vector right; V, vector.

I	aVR	V1	V4
Q Small	Q____	Q No	Q Small
ST Slightly elevated	ST____	ST Isoelectric	ST Isoelectric
T Upright	T____	T Inverted	T Upright
II	aVL	V2	V5
Q Small	Q No	Q No	Q Small
ST Slightly elevated	ST Isoelectric	ST Isoelectric	ST Slightly elevated
T Upright	T Isoelectric	T Inverted	T Upright
III	aVF	V3	V6
Q No	Q No	Q No	Q Small
ST Isoelectric	ST Slightly elevated	ST Isoelectric	ST Slightly elevated
T Upright	T Upright	T Upright	T Upright

- Axis: Normal axis deviation

- Interpretation: Any Q waves in this EKG are too small to be significant. The same is true of any ST changes. This is a pretty normal EKG.

EKG 6.6

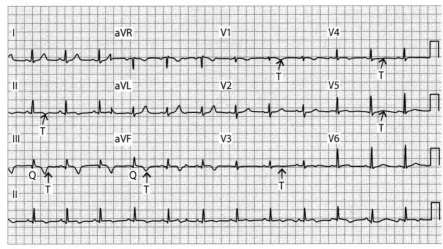

aVF, augmented vector foot; aVL, augmented vector left; aVR, augmented vector right; V, vector.

I	aVR	V1	V4
Q No	Q ____	Q No	Q No
ST Isoelectric	ST ____	ST Isoelectric	ST Isoelectric
T Upright	T ____	T Inverted	T Inverted
II	aVL	V2	V5
Q Small	Q No	Q No	Q No
ST Isoelectric	ST Isoelectric	ST Isoelectric	ST Isoelectric
T Inverted	T Upright	T Upright	T Isoelectric
III	aVF	V3	V6
Q Yes	Q Yes	Q No	Q No
ST Slightly Elevated	ST Slightly elevated	ST Isoelectric	ST Isoelectric
T Inverted	T Inverted	T Isoelectric	T Upright

- Axis: Normal axis deviation

- Interpretation: The Q waves in lead III and aVF look small at first, but they are more than 1/4 the height of the R wave. That makes them significant. The significant Q waves in leads III and aVF indicate the presence of an inferior wall MI. The elevated ST segments in these leads are of concern, even though they are not as severe as one would expect. The inverted T waves suggest that something is certainly going on in the inferior wall.

- Diagnosis: Inferior wall MI with ST elevation is occurring.

Answers to Chapter 7: All Together Now!

EKG 7.1

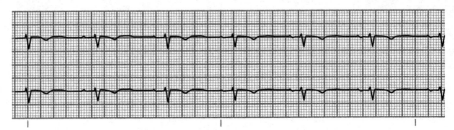

- Rate: Atrial 50 beats per minute (bpm) Ventricular 50 bpm
- Rhythm: Regular
- P wave origin: SA node
- PR interval: 0.20 seconds
- QRS: 0.10 seconds
- QT interval: 0.40 seconds (R-R interval = 1.08 seconds)
- Underlying rhythm: Sinus
- Variant: Bradycardia
- Interpretation: Sinus bradycardia
- Treatment: Only treat sinus bradycardia if the patient is symptomatic. If the patient is symptomatic, atropine is the medication of choice. Dopamine or epinephrine may be used if atropine is not effective or unavailable. If atropine, dopamine, or epinephrine do not work, a transcutaneous or intravenous pacemaker may be placed to control heart rate (Bucher, 2014; Diehl, 2011; Marcum, 2013; Sinz, 2011).
- Discussion
    - **Rate and Rhythm:** There are 5 P waves and 5 QRS complexes between the first and third 3 second markers. That translates to an atrial and ventricular rate of 50 beats per minute. The rhythm is regular.
    - **P wave origin:** The P waves all look alike indicating that they are coming from the same place. That place is assumed to be the patient's SA node.
    - The PR interval is within normal limits.
    - The QT interval is less than 1/2 the R-R interval decreasing the risk of dysrhythmia.
    - **Interpretation:** The impulse is coming from the SA node, but the rate is slow (less than 60 beats per minute). This is a sinus bradycardia.

EKG 7.2

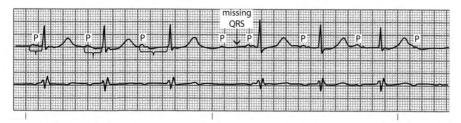

- Rate: Atrial <u>80 bpm</u> Ventricular <u>60 bpm</u>

- Rhythm: Irregular due to missing QRS

- P wave origin: <u>SA node</u>

- PR interval: <u>Progressive</u>

- QRS: <u>0.08 seconds</u>

- QT interval: <u>Not applicable</u>

- Underlying rhythm: <u>Sinus rhythm</u>

- Variant: <u>Second-degree heart block Mobitz I</u>

- Interpretation: <u>Sinus rhythm with second-degree heart block Mobitz I</u>

- Treatment: <u>The first step in treating any dysrhythmia is to check the patient. If the patient is tolerating the rhythm, and it is suspected that this rhythm may be temporary, then a "wait and watch" philosophy may be warranted (Diehl, 2011). The patient's medication list should be evaluated to detect any medications that may cause this rhythm, and those medications withheld. If, however, the patient is not tolerating this rhythm (if the patient is hypotensive, complaining of chest discomfort, etc.), then atropine is the drug of choice to help stimulate the sinoatrial (SA) node further. If some of the P waves are getting through and some are not, the hope is that creating more P waves will allow more to get through. If that does not work, a pacemaker may be necessary (Bucher, 2014; Diehl, 2011).</u>

- Discussion: There are more P waves than QRS complexes. That is usually indicative of some type of heart block. The next step is to evaluate the PR intervals. If the PR interval gets progressively longer before dropping a QRS complex, it is a Mobitz I.

EKG 7.3

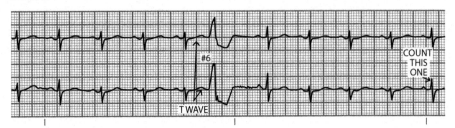

- Rate: Atrial <u>90 bpm</u> Ventricular <u>100 bpm</u>
- Rhythm: Irregular due to early beat (#6)
- P wave origin: <u>SA node</u>
- PR interval: <u>0.16 seconds</u>
- QRS: <u>0.08 seconds/0.14 seconds</u>
- QT interval: <u>0.34 seconds (R-R interval = 0.64 seconds)</u>
- Underlying rhythm: <u>Sinus</u>
- Variant: <u>Beat number 6 is a premature ventricular contraction</u>
- Interpretation: <u>Sinus rhythm with premature ventricular contractions (PVCs)</u>
- Treatment: <u>If the PVCs are occasional, no treatment may be necessary. If, however, they are frequent or if they are coming close to the T waves, the cause of the PVCs needs to be investigated. Perhaps the most common cause is hypoxia, so, if possible, the first order of treatment would be to administer oxygen. Electrolyte levels, especially potassium and magnesium, need to be examined and treated if necessary (Bucher, 2014; Diehl, 2011). Medications, such as amiodarone, procainamide, lidocaine, and/or beta-adrenergic blockers, can be used for control of PVCs (Bucher, 2014; Diehl, 2011).</u>
- Discussion: In this case there are more QRS complexes than P waves. The only time that P waves may be missing are with (a) A-fib (but the rhythm is very irregular), (b) with junctional beats (but the QRS complex is usually narrow), and (c) with ventricular beats. Ventricular beats are usually wide in configuration as with beat number 6.

EKG 7.4

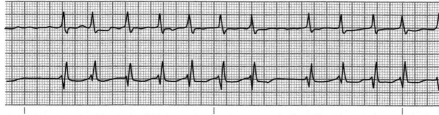

- Rate: Atrial <u>0</u> Ventricular <u>110 bpm</u>
- Rhythm: Irregular
- P wave origin: <u>Not applicable</u>
- PR interval: <u>Not applicable</u>
- QRS: <u>0.14 seconds</u>
- QT interval: <u>Not applicable</u>
- Underlying rhythm: <u>Atrial fibrillation</u>
- Variant: <u>Rate Greater than 100</u>
- Interpretation: <u>Atrial fibrillation (uncontrolled)</u>
- Treatment: <u>Assess the patient for tolerance. A transesophageal echocardiogram is needed to determine the presence of blood clots. If they are present, administer anticoagulants (heparin, warfarin, dabigatran [Pradaxa], apixaban [Eliquis], or rivaroxaban [Xarelto]). If or when blood clots are not present, conversion via medications such as amiodarone or ibutilide, or electrically using synchronized cardioversion is necessary (Bucher, 2014). If cardioversion is not possible, rate control is attempted with medication. Calcium channel blockers such as diltiazem, beta-adrenergic blockers such as metoprolol, or digoxin are used to control the heart rate (Bucher, 2014). The need for anticoagulation may be lifelong.</u>
- Discussion: There are no P waves and the rhythm is irregular. By definition, this is atrial fibrillation. Because the rate is greater than 100, it is considered "uncontrolled." In order to maximize cardiac output, the goal would be to get the heart rate to a "normal" level (60–100 beats per minute) so that ventricular filling and emptying would be maximized.

EKG 7.5

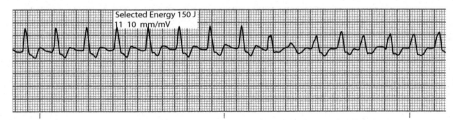

Selected Energy 150 J
11 10 mm/mV

- Rate: Atrial 0 Ventricular 120 bpm
- Rhythm: Regular
- P wave origin: None
- PR interval: Not applicable
- QRS: 0.14 seconds
- QT interval: Not applicable
- Underlying rhythm: Ventricular
- Variant: Tachycardia
- Interpretation: Ventricular tachycardia
- Treatment: Determine responsiveness of the patient. If the patient is conscious, apply oxygen and treat with intravenous amiodarone or lidocaine following advanced cardiac life support (ACLS) protocols. If the patient is conscious but unstable (i.e., has a low blood pressure and symptoms of decompensation), synchronized cardioversion may be needed to terminate the rhythm (Diehl, 2011; Marcum, 2013). If the patient is unresponsive, there is no blood being pumped to the brain and death will ensue within a short time. Treat as if this were V-fib (ventricular fibrillation; Diehl, 2011; Marcum, 2013).
- Discussion: There are no P waves and the QRS complexes are wide. This is a rapid rhythm coming from the ventricles.

EKG 7.6

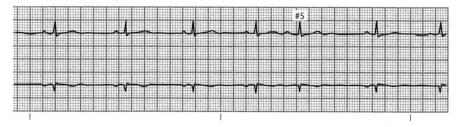

- Rate: Atrial <u>60 bpm</u> Ventricular <u>60 bpm</u>

- Rhythm: Irregular due to early beat (beat #5)

- P wave origin: <u>SA node/atrial (#5)</u>

- PR interval: <u>0.18 seconds/0.24 seconds (#5)</u>

- QRS: <u>0.08 seconds</u>

- QT interval: <u>0.40 seconds (R-R interval = 1.08 seconds)</u>

- Underlying rhythm: <u>Sinus</u>

- Variant: <u>Premature atrial contraction</u>

- Interpretation: <u>Sinus rhythm with premature atrial contractions (PACs)</u>

- Treatment: <u>If there are fewer than six contractions per minute, they are not usually treated (Bucher, 2014; Diehl, 2011). If there are more than six per minute, this may be a sign that worse things are in to come such as atrial tachycardia, atrial flutter, or atrial fibrillation. If at all possible, treat the cause (Bucher, 2014; Diehl, 2011). If this is not possible, or not effective, beta blockers are the preferred medication used in the treatment of PACs (Bucher, 2014).</u>

- Discussion: The P wave for beat number 5 looks a bit different from the other P waves, indicating that it is coming from a different focus than the other P waves are. Because all P waves come from somewhere in the atria (theSA node is also in the atria), beat number 5 must be coming from somewhere in the atria, but not the SA node.

EKG 7.7

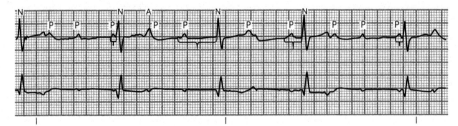

- Rate: Atrial <u>100 bpm</u> Ventricular <u>40 bpm</u>

- Rhythm: Atrial regular and ventricular regular

- P wave origin: <u>SA node</u>

- PR interval: <u>Variable</u>

- QRS: <u>0.10 seconds</u>

- QT interval: <u>Not applicable</u>

- Underlying rhythm: <u>Sinus rhythm</u>

- Variant: <u>Complete heart block</u>

- Interpretation: <u>Third-degree (complete) heart block</u>

- Treatment: <u>Pacemaker</u>

- Discussion: There are more P waves than QRS complexes. When that happens, some type of block is present. The next step is to look at the PR intervals. When they do not have any pattern, it is a third-degree heart block. The atrial rhythm is regular, and the ventricular rhythm is regular, but none of the atrial impulses (P waves) are getting through the atrioventricular (AV) node. The SA node continues to put out P waves regularly not "knowing" what the response is. For that reason, the P waves "bump" into T waves and QRS complexes causing distortions, so often the P waves do not look alike. The ventricles do not sense any impulses coming from above so they act as the backup pacemaker but at a rate less than 40 bpm. The only reliable treatment for this is a pacemaker. Atropine may be ordered, and that may produce more P waves, but none are getting through.

EKG 7.8

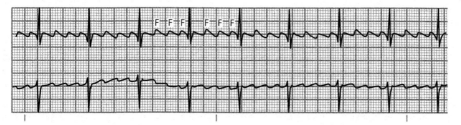

- Rate: Atrial <u>320 bpm</u> Ventricular <u>80 bpm</u>

- Rhythm: Regular

- P wave origin: <u>Atria</u>

- PR interval: <u>Not applicable</u>

- QRS: <u>0.08 seconds</u>

- QT interval: <u>Not applicable</u>

- Underlying rhythm: <u>Atrial</u>

- Variant: <u>Flutter waves</u>

- Interpretation: <u>Atrial flutter</u>

- Treatment: <u>Electrical cardioversion or cardioversion via medications such as ibutilide (Corvert) is necessary (Bucher, 2014; Marcum, 2013). Once converted, medications, such as amiodarone, flecainide (Tambocor), or dronedarone (Multaq), are used to maintain sinus rhythm (Bucher, 2014). If this cannot be done, rate control using calcium channel blockers or beta-adrenergic blockers is attempted (Bucher, 2014). Anticoagulation therapy may be needed to reduce the risk of thromboembolism (Diehl, 2011).</u>

- Discussion: Each QRS has lots of P waves. However, each is allowed only one. Where there are more, they are not P waves but flutter waves (F waves). That is diagnostic of atrial flutter.

EKG 7.9

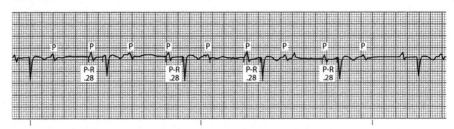

- Rate: Atrial <u>90 bpm</u> Ventricular <u>50 bpm</u>
- Rhythm: Regular
- P wave origin: <u>SA node</u>
- PR interval: <u>0.28 seconds (consistent)</u>
- QRS: <u>0.08 seconds</u>
- QT interval: <u>Not applicable</u>
- Underlying rhythm: <u>Sinus</u>
- Variant: <u>Second-degree heart block (Mobitz II)</u>
- Interpretation: <u>Sinus rhythm with second-degree AV block Mobitz II</u>
- Treatment: <u>This is a second-degree heart block, meaning that some impulses are getting through and others are not. It is unpredictable and that's what makes it dangerous. Yet, because some of the P waves are getting through, atropine is still the drug of choice, used in the hope that creating more P waves will allow more to get through. Otherwise, a temporary pacemaker may be needed while awaiting the insertion of a permanent pacemaker (Bucher, 2014; Diehl, 2011).</u>
- Discussion: There are more P waves than QRS complexes. This indicates that a block is present. The next step is to evaluate the PR intervals. If they are consistent, as in this case, it is a second-degree heart block, Mobitz II.

EKG 7.10

I	aVR	V1	V4
Q No	Q ___	Q No	Q Yes
ST Isoelectric	ST ___	ST Slight elevation	ST Slight elevation
T Isoelectric	T ___	T Inverted	T Isoelectric
II	aVL	V2	V5
Q Yes	Q No	Q No	Q Small
ST Isoelectric	ST Isoelectric	ST Isoelectric	ST Isoelectric
T Isoelectric	T Isoelectric	T Inverted	T Isoelectric
III	aVF	V3	V6
Q Yes	Q Yes	Q No	Q Small
ST Isoelectric	ST Isoelectric	ST Slight elevation	ST Isoelectric
T Isoelectric	T Isoelectric	T Inverted	T Upright

- Axis: Normal axis deviation

- Interpretation: There are significant Q waves in leads II, III, and augmented vector foot (aVF), indicating an inferior wall myocardial infarction (MI), but there is no ST elevation or depression that would indicate the ischemia that would be required to cause an MI. Therefore, this MI is old. However, the isoelectric T wave indicates that something is going on, and further assessment is needed. There is a huge Q wave in lead V4, but also no ischemia. Initially, V3 looks like a large Q wave, but there is a tiny positive deflection just before the downward deflection that is an R wave making the main deflection an S wave and not a Q wave. The EKG does look suspicious, however, especially in the light of the slight ST segment elevation in V3 and V4. The patient's presentation and other diagnostics should be used to make the final determination. Old EKGs should be used for comparison.

EKG 7.11

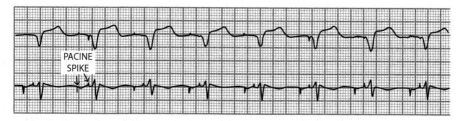

PACINE
SPIKE

- Rate: Atrial <u>70 bpm</u> Ventricular <u>70 bpm</u>
- Rhythm: Regular
- P wave origin: <u>Atrial paced</u>
- PR interval: <u>0.16 seconds</u>
- QRS: <u>0.14 seconds–paced</u>
- QT interval: <u>Not applicable</u>
- Underlying rhythm: <u>Atrial–ventricular pacing</u>
- Variant: <u>Not applicable</u>
- Interpretation: <u>Atrial–ventricular pacing 100%</u>
- Treatment: <u>Not available</u>
- Discussion: There are pacing spikes before each P wave and each QRS complex. Both chambers are being paced. That's a good thing.

EKG 7.12

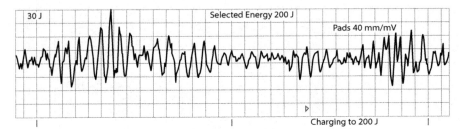

- Rate: Atrial <u>0</u> Ventricular <u>Too numerous to count</u>

- Rhythm: Irregular

- P wave origin: <u>Not applicable</u>

- PR interval: <u>Not applicable</u>

- QRS: <u>Not applicable</u>

- QT interval: <u>Not applicable</u>

- Underlying rhythm: <u>Ventricular tachycardia</u>

- Variant: <u>Torsades de Pointes</u>

- Interpretation: <u>Torsades de Pointes</u>

- Treatment: <u>Prevent by checking and correcting electrolyte abnormalities before this occurs. Discontinue medications that can prolong QT interval. Treat with intravenous (IV) magnesium, isoproterenol, or phenytoin along with electrocardioversion if needed (Bucher, 2014; Diehl, 2011; Marcum, 2013; Sinz, 2011).</u>

- Discussion: This is a preventable rhythm. It is caused by magnesium deficiency. Maintaining adequate magnesium levels is critical.

EKG 7.13

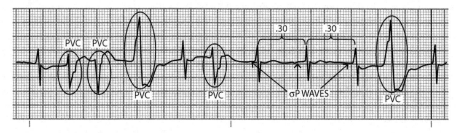

PVC, premature ventricular contraction.

- Rate: Atrial Unable to count Ventricular 100 bpm
- Rhythm: Irregular due to premature beats
- P wave origin: Unable to determine
- PR interval: Not applicable
- QRS: Variable widths
- QT interval: Not applicable
- Underlying rhythm: Atrial versus junctional
- Variant: Premature ventricular contractions

- Interpretation: Supraventricular tachycardia with multifocal PVCs
- Treatment: There is a little more urgency in treating multifocal PVCs than in treating unifocal PVCs. However, the criteria and treatment are otherwise similar. If the PVCs are infrequent, there may be no treatment necessary. Otherwise, the first order of treatment would be to administer oxygen.
  Electrolyte levels, especially potassium and magnesium, need to be examined and treated if necessary (Bucher, 2014; Diehl, 2011). Medications, such as amiodarone, procainamide, lidocaine, and/or beta-adrenergic blockers, can be used for control of PVCs (Bucher, 2014; Diehl, 2011).

- Discussion
  - **Rate and rhythm:** I cannot see P waves, but the QRS complexes (except for beats 2, 3, 4, and 10) are narrow and look fairly normal, indicating a supraventricular focus. The ventricular rate is 100 bpm. I can see beats 7, 8, and quite clearly and believe that these are indicative of the patient's underlying rhythm. That rhythm seems regular, ruling out atrial fibrillation (A-fib) as an underlying rhythm. However, the overall rhythm is irregular due to early beats 2, 3, 4, 6, and 10.
  - **P-wave origin and PR interval:** Because the P waves are not seen, the underlying rhythm could be junctional in origin. However, there is a chance that the P waves are small and difficult to see, and that would make this, at least, atrial in origin. I would need a longer strip of just the underlying rhythm to be sure, so I will compromise and call this supraventricular (that really means "I don't know, but it's not coming from the ventricles"). Because there is no clearly defined P wave, there is no PR interval.

- **QRS complexes:** The QRS complexes that make up the underlying rhythm (beats 1, 5, 7, 8, and 9) look the same and are narrow, indicating that they are coming from the same place and traveling through the same tissue. Most likely, that tissue is the normal conductive pathway of the ventricles. The remaining QRS complexes all are wide and look different from one another. Actually, beats 2 and 6 look similar and beats 3 and 10 look similar, but 2 and 6 do not look like 3 and 10. This indicates there are at least two ectopic foci in the ventricles. Add to that beat number 3 does not look like any of the other beats. That makes three ectopic foci. This is an irritable ventricle, and the risk of lethal arrhythmia is very high.

EKG 7.14

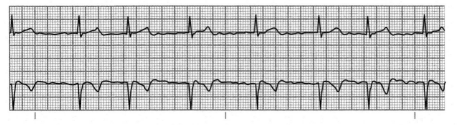

- Rate: Atrial <u>0</u> Ventricular <u>60 bpm</u>
- Rhythm: <u>Irregular</u>
- P wave origin: <u>Not applicable</u>
- PR interval: <u>Not applicable</u>
- QRS: <u>0.08 seconds</u>
- QT interval: <u>0.40 seconds (R-R interval = 0.76 seconds)</u>
- Underlying rhythm: <u>Atrial fibrillation</u>
- Variant: <u>Not applicable</u>
- Interpretation: <u>Atrial fibrillation</u>
- Treatment: <u>Assess the patient for tolerance. Transesophageal echocardiogram is needed to determine the presence of blood clots. If they are present, anticoagulation therapy is needed (heparin, warfarin, dabigatran [Pradaxa], apixaban [Eliquis], or rivaroxaban [Xarelto]). If or when blood clots are not present, conversion therapy via medications such as amiodarone or ibutilide, or electrically using synchronized cardioversion is necessary (Bucher, 2014). If cardioversion is not possible, rate control with calcium channel blockers such as diltiazem, beta-adrenergic blockers such as metoprolol, or digoxin is necessary (Bucher, 2014). The need for anticoagulation may be lifelong.</u>
- Discussion: It's important to remember that A-fib is not a disease, but a symptom. Something has caused it to happen. If we can determine the cause, it is to be hoped that we can prevent it from happening again. Often, however, the cause is unknown, or, if known, is not treatable. In those cases, control is what should be sought. Keeping the rate within a normal range will help maximize cardiac output.

EKG 7.15

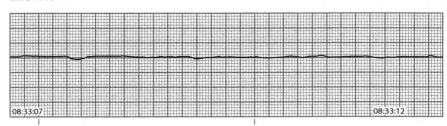

08:33:07   08:33:12

Source: Knechtel, M. (2017). *EKGs for nurse practitioners and physician assistants* (p. 176). New York, NY: Springer Publishing.

- Rate: Atrial 0 Ventricular 0

- Rhythm: Not applicable

- P wave origin: Not applicable

- PR interval: Not applicable

- QRS: Not applicable

- QT interval: Not applicable

- Underlying rhythm: Asystole

- Variant: Asystole

- Interpretation: Asystole

- Treatment: The fact is if someone is truly asystolic, there is no hope. Nothing is going to bring this person back. He or she is dead. If that is the attitude, then, why try? If you have resigned yourself to this thought process, you have condemned your patient to death. There is, however, another way to look at this.

- Discussion: What if this is not asystole? What if, instead, this is a very fine ventricular fibrillation? We can treat ventricular fibrillation. If we think of asystole as a fine ventricular fibrillation, then our goal will be to convert the fine fibrillation to a coarse fibrillation so that we can defibrillate with a better chance of success. The drug of choice used to do this is epinephrine (Adrenalin). Epinephrine, however, will not work unless we get circulation going, so cardiopulmonary resuscitation (CPR) will be required followed by ACLS.

EKG 7.16

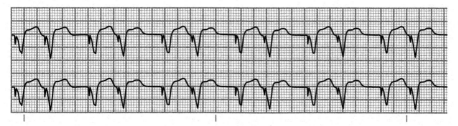

- Rate: Atrial 0 Ventricular 100 bpm
- Rhythm: Irregular
- P wave origin: Not applicable
- PR interval: Not applicable
- QRS: 0.12 seconds
- QT interval: Not applicable
- Underlying rhythm: Ventricular pacing
- Variant: Not applicable
- Interpretation: Ventricular pacing 100%
- Treatment: None required
- Discussion: There is a pacing spike before each QRS complex indicating that the QRS complexes are being paced. There are no P waves so there is no atrial activity. This is 100% ventricular pacing.

EKG 7.17

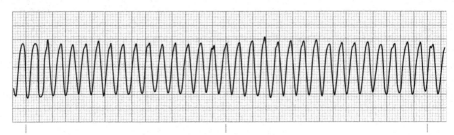

- Rate: Atrial <u>0</u> Ventricular <u>320 bpm</u>
- Rhythm: Regular
- P wave origin: <u>Not applicable</u>
- PR interval: <u>Not applicable</u>
- QRS: <u>Not applicable</u>
- QT interval: <u>Not applicable</u>
- Underlying rhythm: <u>Ventricular tachycardia</u>
- Variant: <u>Not applicable</u>
- Interpretation: <u>Ventricular tachycardia</u>
- Treatment: <u>Determine responsiveness of the patient. If the patient is conscious, apply oxygen and treat with intravenous amiodarone or lidocaine following ACLS protocols. If the patient is conscious but unstable (i.e., has a low blood pressure and symptoms of decompensation), synchronized cardioversion may be needed to terminate the rhythm (Diehl, 2014; Marcum, 2013). If the patient is unresponsive, there is no blood being pumped to the brain and death will ensue within a short time. Treat as if this were V-fib.</u>

EKG 7.18

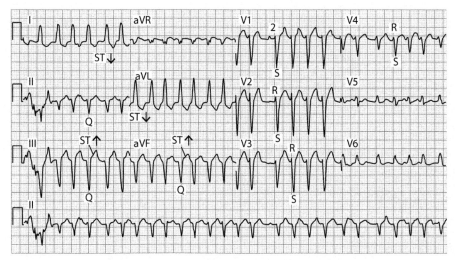

aVF, augmented vector foot; aVL, augmented vector left; aVR, augmented vector right; V, vector.

I	aVR	V1	V4
Q No	Q ___	Q No	Q No
ST Depressed	ST ___	ST Slightly elevated	ST Slightly elevated
T Inverted	T ___	T Upright	T Upright
II	aVL	V2	V5
Q Yes	Q No	Q No	Q No
ST Normal	ST Depressed	ST Slightly elevated	ST Depressed
T Upright	T Inverted	T Upright	T ___
III	aVF	V3	V6
Q Yes	Q Yes	Q No	Q No
ST Elevated	ST Elevated	ST Slightly elevated	ST Depressed
T Upright	T Upright	T Upright	T Upright

- Axis: Left axis deviation

- Interpretation: Large Q waves in leads II, III, and aVF indicate an inferior wall M). ST elevations in those same leads may indicate that the MI is occurring now. However, this may also indicate an old MI with new ischemia. At any rate, the ischemia is the issue and could lead to arrhythmia and sudden death. The inverted T waves in leads I and aVL are also a concern as is the slight ST elevations in leads V1, V2, V3, and V4.

- Discussion: This is the dreaded STEMI (ST elevation myocardial infarction). The assumption should be that the MI is happening as we view it. The ischemia needs to be treated as quickly as possible. Thrombolytics, angioplasty with stenting, or coronary bypass are all options.

EKG 7.19

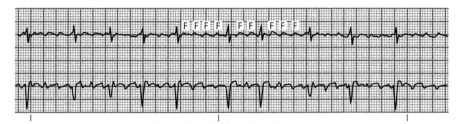

- Rate: Atrial <u>270 bpm</u> Ventricular <u>90 bpm</u>

- Rhythm: Regular

- P wave origin: <u>Atrial</u>

- PR interval: <u>Not applicable</u>

- QRS: <u>0.12 seconds</u>

- QT interval: <u>Not applicable</u>

- Underlying rhythm: <u>Atrial flutter</u>

- Variant: <u>F waves</u>

- Interpretation: <u>Atrial flutter</u>

- Treatment: <u>The primary goal is to convert the atrial flutter back to a sinus rhythm.</u>
  <u>This can be done by way of electrical cardioversion or the use of medications such</u>
  <u>as ibutilide (Corvert) (Bucher, 2014; Marcum, 2013). Once converted, medications,</u>
  <u>such as amiodarone, flecainide (Tambocor), and dronedarone (Multaq), are used to</u>
  <u>maintain sinus rhythm (Bucher, 2014).</u>
  <u>If conversion cannot be achieved, rate control is needed to improve cardiac</u>
  <u>function. This can be done using calcium channel blockers or beta-adrenergic</u>
  <u>blockers (Bucher, 2014). Anticoagulation may be needed to reduce the risk of</u>
  <u>thromboembolism (Diehl, 2011).</u>

- Discussion: Each QRS is allowed only one P wave. If there are more than one, and
  the rate is fast enough, the diagnosis is atrial flutter. Atrial flutter is the second most
  lethal atrial dysrhythmia. Cardiac output may be decreased. It may deteriorate into
  atrial fibrillation. It may place the patient at greater risk for stroke and/or pulmonary
  embolism.

EKG 7.20

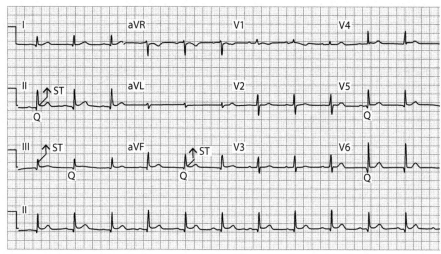

aVF, augmented vector foot; aVL, augmented vector left; aVR, augmented vector right; V, vector.

I	aVR	V1	V4
Q Small	Q ___	Q No	Q No
ST Isoelectric	ST ___	ST Isoelectric	ST Slightly elevated
T Upright	T ___	T Inverted	T Upright
II	aVL	V2	V5
Q Yes	Q No	Q No	Q Small
ST Elevated	ST Isoelectric	ST Isoelectric	ST Slightly elevated
T Upright	T Isoelectric	T Upright	T Upright
III	aVF	V3	V6
Q Yes	Q Yes	Q No	Q Yes
ST Elevated	ST Elevated	ST Isoelectric	ST Isoelectric
T Upright	T Upright	T Upright	T Upright

- Axis: Normal axis deviation

- Interpretation: There are small but significant Q waves in leads II, III, and aVF, indicating an inferior wall MI. There is also ST segment elevation in those leads, but they are not very high and of questionable significance. There are also very small Q waves in leads I and V5 with a larger Q wave in V6, leading to a possible infarction in the lateral leads. However, the ST segments are isoelectric in those leads with the exception of a slight elevation in V5. Overall, this EKG is suggestive of an inferior wall MI of questionable age and possibly an old lateral wall MI. The EKG should be compared to older EKGs if possible, and the patient treated according to his or her clinical picture and evaluation of other diagnostic tests.

- Discussion: What places the patient in danger is the presence of ischemia. The ischemia that is present in this patient is minimal, but still of concern. Remember that the higher the elevation or the lower the depression, the greater the ischemia. However, even small amounts of ischemia can lead to dysrhythmia. Look to see the patient's symptoms and weigh the possibility that they are being caused by the ischemia seen on the EKG.

EKG 7.21

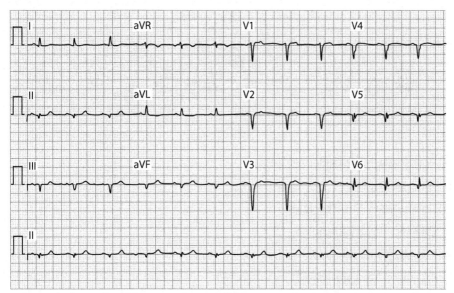

aVF, augmented vector foot; aVL, augmented vector left; aVR, augmented vector right; V, vector.

I	aVR	V1	V4
Q No	Q ___	Q No	Q Yes
ST Isoelectric	ST ___	ST Isoelectric	ST Isoelectric
T Upright	T ___	T Upright	T Isoelectric
II	aVL	V2	V5
Q Yes	Q No	Q Yes	Q Yes
ST Isoelectric	ST Isoelectric	ST Isoelectric	ST Isoelectric
T Upright	T Inverted	T Upright	T Upright
III	aVF	V3	V6
Q Yes	Q Yes	Q Yes	Q Yes
ST Isoelectric	ST Isoelectric	ST Isoelectric	ST Isoelectric
T Upright	T Upright	T Upright	T Upright

- Axis: Extreme left axis deviation

- Interpretation: There are significant Q waves in all leads except for aVL. This is suggestive of massive global infarction, but there is no ST elevation or depression, indicating that there are no active issues at present. The person has had an anterior MI, an inferior MI, and a lateral MI sometime in the past (either at separate times or all at once). Reviewing past EKGs might help piece together the cardiac history of this patient. Evaluate the patient's condition and treat accordingly.

- Discussion: Ischemia is what places the patient at risk. There is no ST elevation or depression in this EKG making this EKG benign relative to patient risk.

EKG 7.22

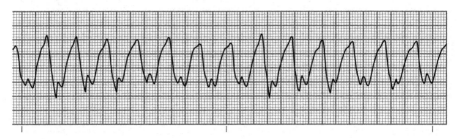

- Rate: Atrial <u>0</u> Ventricular <u>140 bpm</u>

- Rhythm: Regular

- P wave origin: <u>Not applicable</u>

- PR interval: <u>Not applicable</u>

- QRS: <u>0.20 seconds</u>

- QT interval: <u>Not applicable</u>

- Underlying rhythm: <u>Ventricular tachycardia</u>

- Variant: <u>Ventricular tachycardia</u>

- Interpretation: <u>Ventricular tachycardia</u>

- Treatment: <u>Determine responsiveness of the patient. If the patient is conscious, apply oxygen and treat with intravenous amiodarone or lidocaine following ACLS protocols. If the patient is conscious but unstable (i.e., has a low blood pressure and symptoms of decompensation), synchronized cardioversion may be needed to terminate the rhythm (Diehl, 2011: Marcum, 2013). If the patient is unresponsive, there is no blood being pumped to the brain and death will ensue within a short time. Treat as if this were V-fib.</u>

- Discussion

  - **Rate:** There are no P waves so there is no atrial rate. The ventricular rate is 140 beats per minute. This is very rapid. The diagnosis is made.
  - Since there are no P waves there is no PR interval.
  - **QRS:** The QRS complexes are wide and have no P waves. That makes the QRS complexes ventricular in origin.

EKG 7.23

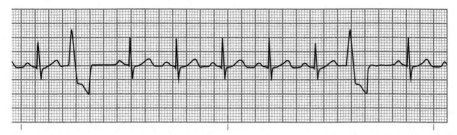

- Rate: Atrial <u>70 bpm</u> Ventricular <u>90 bpm</u>
- Rhythm: Irregular due to beat numbers 2 and 8 being early
- P wave origin: <u>SA node</u>
- PR interval: <u>0.18 seconds</u>
- QRS: <u>0.08 seconds/0.18 seconds</u>
- QT interval: <u>0.36 seconds (R-R interval = 0.68 seconds)</u>
- Underlying rhythm: <u>Sinus rhythm</u>
- Variant: <u>Unifocal premature ventricular contractions</u>
- Interpretation: <u>Sinus rhythm with unifocal PVCs</u>
- Treatment: <u>If PVCs are occasional and not close to the T waves of the patient's normal beats, they probably will not need treatment. However, if they are more than "occasional" (more than six per minute) or close to the T waves, the cause of the PVCs needs to be investigated. Perhaps the most common cause is hypoxia, so, if possible, the first order of treatment would be to administer oxygen (Bucher, 2014; Diehl, 2011). Electrolyte levels, especially potassium and magnesium, need to be examined and treated if necessary (Bucher, 2014; Diehl, 2011; Sinz, 2011). Medications, such as amiodarone, procainamide, lidocaine, and/or beta-adrenergic blockers, can be used for control of PVCs.</u>
- Discussion
  - **Rate and rhythm:** There are more ventricular beats than atrial beats. The beats that do not have P waves are also coming early causing the rhythm to be irregular.
  - **PR interval:** Normal when present and consistent.
  - **QRS:** The QRS complexes are all within normal ranges with the exception of the early beats which are wide. The wideness and the lack of a P wave make me believe that these are ventricular beats in origin, and the fact that they come early make them PVCs.

EKG 7.24

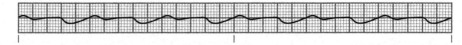

Source: Landrum, M. A. (2013). *Fast facts about EKGs for nurses: The rules of identifying EKGs in a nutshell* (p. 100). New York, NY: Springer Publishing.

- Rate: Atrial <u>0</u> Ventricular <u>0</u>

- Rhythm: Not applicable

- P wave origin: <u>Not applicable</u>

- PR interval: <u>Not applicable</u>

- QRS: <u>Not applicable</u>

- QT interval: <u>Not applicable</u>

- Underlying rhythm: <u>Ventricular fibrillation</u>

- Variant: <u>Not applicable</u>

- Interpretation: <u>Ventricular fibrillation</u>

- Treatment: <u>Assess the patient. If the patient is awake or breathing, he is not in ventricular fibrillation. Check the patient's leads. If the patient is unresponsive, begin CPR and call for help. Institute ACLS protocols as soon as possible.</u>
  <u>When ventricular first starts, the rhythm is "coarse" looking. As time goes on, the rhythm will become finer and finer until it becomes a straight line. The progressive deterioration of the rhythm (as the rhythm becomes "finer") indicates the increasing level of toxicity in the heart muscle. This is of great concern because the more toxic the muscle is, the less likely it is to respond to defibrillation. Fortunately, there is a medication that has the unique ability to convert fine fibrillation back into coarse fibrillation.</u>
  <u>Epinephrine (Adrenalin) is that medication. Epinephrine is a catecholamine that is also a potent vasoconstrictor with a very short duration (Comerford, 2016). It is possible that the sudden constriction of the coronary arteries may force "toxic" blood out of the heart and then the relaxation of the arteries soon afterward may "suck" oxygenated blood in. In that way, it can convert the fine fibrillation back to the coarse fibrillation. For this reason, this medication is given every 3 to 5 minutes during a cardiac arrest (code) situation. Again, epinephrine will not break the rhythm. It will only make it more susceptible to defibrillation. However, the cause of the fibrillation is still not known and may never be known, so antiarrhythmics are used to prevent the heart from going back into fibrillation once defibrillation successfully terminates the fibrillation. Amiodarone and lidocaine are two of those antiarrhythmic medications. Use per ACLS protocols.</u>

- Discussion: This patient is dead. He will not be breathing. He will not be speaking. He will not be responsive. If he is doing any of those things, do not shock him. Check his leads. If a lead becomes disconnected, it will often look like V-fib. It is not.

If it is truly V-fib, the patient is dead. You cannot make him deader. The worst you can do is maintain that level of dead. Otherwise, all you can do is make him better. You may break ribs doing CPR. You may burn the chest using the defibrillator, but if the patient wakes up and complains of sore ribs and chest, you have done your job. It beats the alternative.

EKG 7.25

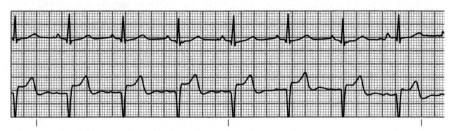

- Rate: Atrial <u>70 bpm</u> Ventricular <u>70 bpm</u>

- Rhythm: Regular

- P wave origin: <u>SA node</u>

- PR interval: <u>0.16 seconds</u>

- QRS: <u>0.08 seconds</u>

- QT interval: <u>0.42 seconds (R-R interval = 0.86 seconds)</u>

- Underlying rhythm: <u>Sinus</u>

- Variant: <u>None</u>

- Interpretation: <u>Normal sinus rhythm</u>

- Treatment: <u>None</u>

- Discussion: Everything in this rhythm strip is normal. It is what we hope all our patients have. There is nothing to do. I pray that all of the readers of this book have this rhythm forever.

References

Bucher, L. (2014). Nursing management: Dysrhythmias. In S. Lewis, S. Dirksen, M. Heitkemper, L. Bucher, & M. Harding (Eds.), *Medical-surgical nursing: Assessment and management of clinical problems* (9th ed., pp. 787–809). St. Louis, MO: Elsevier Mosby.

Comerford, K. (Ed.). (2016). *Nursing 2016 drug handbook*. Philadelphia, PA: Wolters Kluwer.

Diehl, T. (Ed.). (2011). *ECG interpretation made incredibly easy!* Philadelphia, PA: Lippincott Williams & Wilkins.

Green, J. M., & Chiaramida, A. J. (2015). *12-Lead EKG confidence* (3rd ed.). New York, NY: Springer Publishing.

Knechtel, M. (2017). *EKGs for the nurse practitioners and physician assistants* (2nd ed.). New York, NY: Springer Publishing.

Landrum, M.A. (2014). *Fast facts about EKGs for nurses: The rules of identifying EKGs in a nutshell*. New York, NY: Springer Publishing.

Marcum, J. (2013). Dysrhythmia interpretation and management. In M. L. Sole, D. Klein, & M. Moseley (Eds.), *Introduction to critical care nursing* (6th ed., (pp. 94–139). St. Louis, MO: Elsevier Saunders.

Sinz, E. (Ed.). (2011). *Advanced cardiovascular life support provider manual*. Dallas, TX: American Heart Association.

Questions and comments about *Fast Facts Workbook for Cardiac Dysrhythmias and 12-Lead EKGs* may be directed to the author at Paul.Desmarais@ucf.edu.

Index

A-fib. *See* atrial fibrillation (A-fib)
accelerated idioventricular rhythms, 32, 39, 146, 156
ACLS. *See* advanced cardiac life support (ACLS)
Adenocard. *See* adenosine (Adenocard), for sinus tachycardia
adenosine (Adenocard), for sinus tachycardia, 128
Adrenalin. *See* epinephrine (Adrenalin)
advanced cardiac life support (ACLS), 35, 36, 155, 162, 163, 165, 166, 167, 168, 169, 170, 172, 173, 176, 177, 179, 183, 184, 185, 214, 226, 228, 234, 236
amiodarone
    for atrial fibrillation, 132, 136, 213, 225
    for atrial flutter, 116, 131, 134, 135, 217, 230
    and idioventricular rhythms, 155, 184
    for premature junctional beats, 16, 140, 144, 164
    for premature ventricular contractions, 33, 34, 35, 154, 174, 180, 181, 212
        couplets, 159
        multifocal, 157, 223
        unifocal, 235
    for ventricular ectopic activity, 160, 161
    for ventricular fibrillation, 163, 167, 169, 173, 183, 236
    for ventricular tachycardia, 165, 176, 177, 214, 228, 234
anterior wall ischemia, 93, 206
anterior wall myocardial infarction, 89, 118, 233
    old, 92, 205
antiarrhythmics
    for idioventricular rhythms, 155
    for ventricular fibrillation, 167, 169, 173, 183, 236

anticoagulants/anticoagulation
    for atrial fibrillation, 132, 136, 213, 225
    for atrial flutter, 131, 134, 135, 217, 230
antipyretics, for sinus tachycardia, 128
apixaban (Eliquis), for atrial fibrillation, 132, 136, 213, 225
asystole, 36, 49, 60, 112, 170, 185, 226
atrial fibrillation (A-fib), 4, 11, 111, 130, 132–133, 134, 135, 145, 215, 225. *See also* ventricular fibrillation (V-fib)
    controlled, 14, 136–137
    vs. premature ventricular contractions, 33
    uncontrolled, 101, 213
    with ventricular ectopic activity (couplet), 50, 171
    with ventricular ectopic activity and triplet, 42, 160
atrial flutter, 4, 10, 12, 13, 105, 116, 130, 131, 134, 135, 215, 217, 230
atrial pacing, 63, 67, 71, 188, 192, 196
atrial rate, 3
atrial rhythms, 3–4
    atrial fibrillation, 11, 14, 33, 101, 111, 132–133, 136–137, 213, 225
    atrial flutter, 4, 10, 12, 13, 105, 116, 131, 134, 135, 217, 230
    normal sinus rhythm, 5, 6, 122, 126, 127, 238
    premature atrial contractions, sinus rhythm with, 9, 103, 130, 215
    sinus bradycardia, 8, 98, 129, 210
    sinus tachycardia, 7, 128
atrial sensing/ventricular pacing, 62, 66, 70, 74, 191, 195, 199
atrial tachycardia, 130, 215
atrioventricular (AV) block, 4, 23
    first-degree, 23, 24
        sinus rhythm with, 17, 25, 56, 140–141, 148, 180

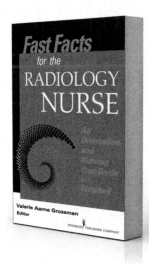